# THE BIG BOOK OF..... RIFFS

## JUST THE RIFFS!

HAL LEONARD EUROPE
DISTRIBUTED BY MUSIC SALES

EXCLUSIVE DISTRIBUTORS:
MUSIC SALES LIMITED
8/9 FRITH STREET, LONDON W1D 3JB, ENGLAND.
MUSIC SALES PTY LIMITED
120 ROTHSCHILD AVENUE, ROSEBERY, NSW 2018, AUSTRALIA.

ORDER NO. HLE90001725
ISBN 0-7119-9718-7
THIS BOOK © COPYRIGHT 2002 BY HAL LEONARD EUROPE.

COVER DESIGN BY FRESH LEMON.
PRINTED IN THE USA.


YOUR GUARANTEE OF QUALITY:
AS PUBLISHERS, WE STRIVE TO PRODUCE EVERY
BOOK TO THE HIGHEST COMMERCIAL STANDARDS.
THE BOOK HAS BEEN CAREFULLY DESIGNED TO
MAKE PLAYING FROM IT A REAL PLEASURE.
THROUGHOUT, THE PRINTING AND BINDING HAVE
BEEN PLANNED TO ENSURE A STURDY, ATTRACTIVE
PUBLICATION WHICH SHOULD GIVE YEARS OF ENJOYMENT.
IF YOUR COPY FAILS TO MEET OUR HIGH STANDARDS,
PLEASE INFORM US AND WE WILL GLADLY REPLACE IT.

WWW.MUSICSALES.COM

# All Blues

By Miles Davis

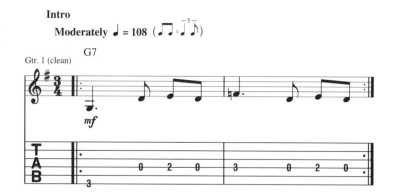

# All Day and All of the Night

Words and Music by Ray Davies

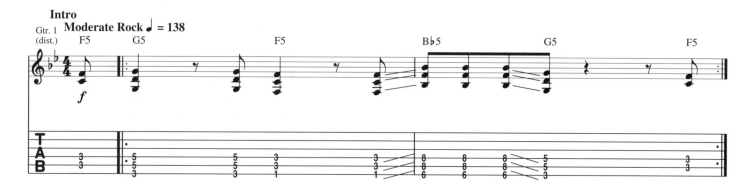

# All Right Now

Words and Music by Paul Rodgers and Andy Fraser

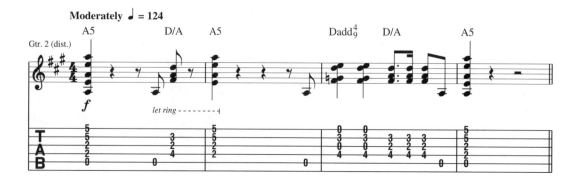

# All Your Love (I Miss Loving)

**Words and Music by Otis Rush**

* Chords symbols reflect overall harmony.

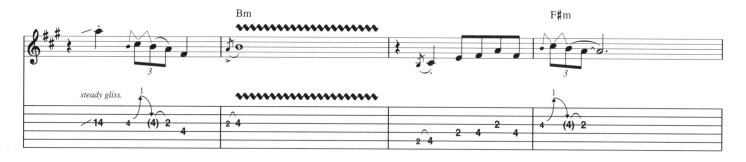

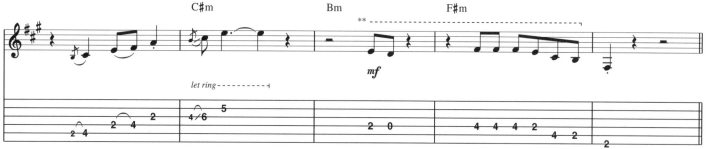

**Played as even eighth notes.

# Amanda

**Words and Music by Tom Scholz**

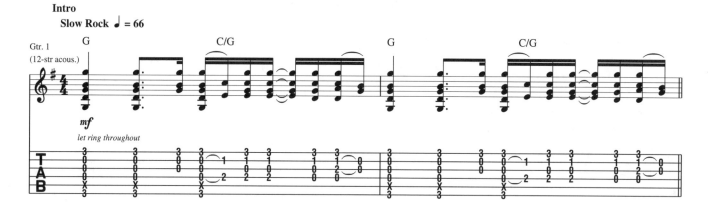

# American Woman

Written by Burton Cummings, Randy Bachman, Gary Peterson and Jim Kale

# And I Love Her

Words and Music by John Lennon and Paul McCartney

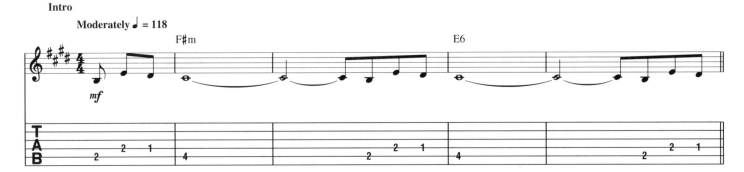

# Annie's Song

Words and Music by John Denver

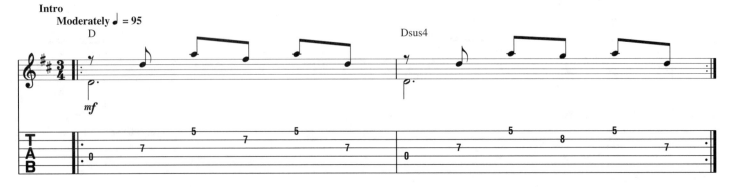

# Angie

**Words and Music by Mick Jagger and Keith Richards**

Intro

Slowly ♩ = 73

# Barracuda

**Words and Music by Roger Fisher, Nancy Wilson, Ann Wilson and Michael Derosier**

Intro

Moderately fast Rock ♩ = 132

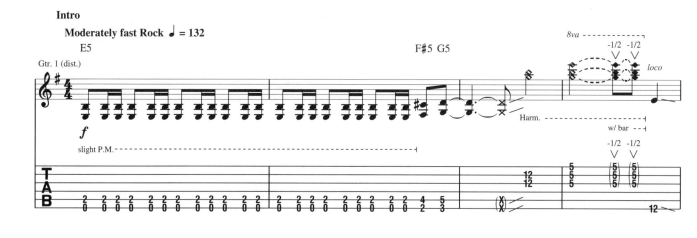

# Authority Song

**Words and Music by John Mellencamp**

Tuning:
(low to high) D–A–D–G–B–D

### Intro

Moderately fast ♩ = 157

N.C.

Gtr. 1 (clean)

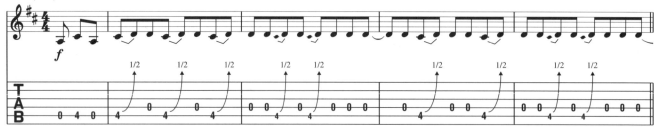

# Back Door Man

**Written by Willie Dixon**

### Intro

Moderate Blues ♩ = 88

*A7

Gtr. 1 (clean)

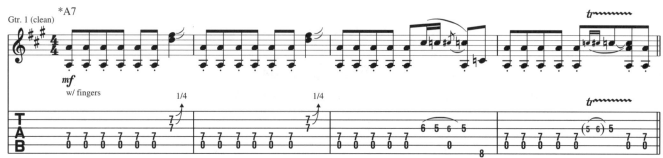

* Chord symbols reflect basic harmony.

# Bad Love

**Words and Music by Eric Clapton and Mick Jones**

### Intro

Moderate Rock ♩ = 124

Gtr. (dist.)

N.C.

# Ballroom Blitz

**Words and Music by Mike Chapman and Nicky Chinn**

Moderately ♩ = 108

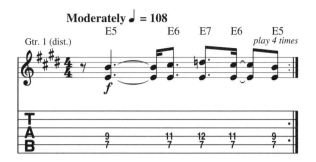

# Bang a Gong (Get It On)

**Words and Music by Marc Bolan**

Moderate Rock ♩ = 127

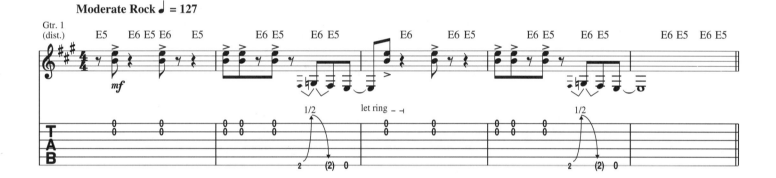

# The Bed's Too Big Without You

**Written and Composed by Sting**

Intro
Half-Time Reggae Feel ♩ = 182

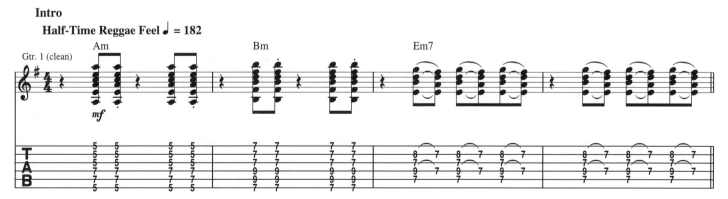

# Big City Nights

**Words and Music by Klaus Meine and Rudolf Schenker**

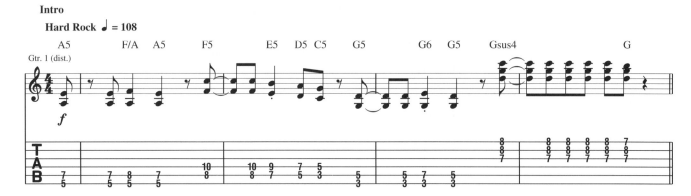

# Birthday

**Words and Music by John Lennon and Paul McCartney**

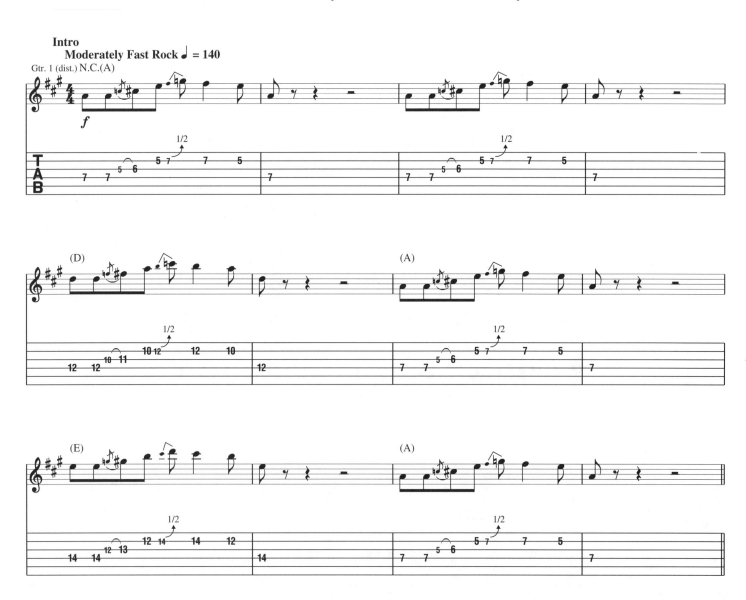

# Black Hearted Woman

**Words and Music by Gregg Allman**

# Cold Shot

**Words and Music by Mike Kindred and W.C. Clark**

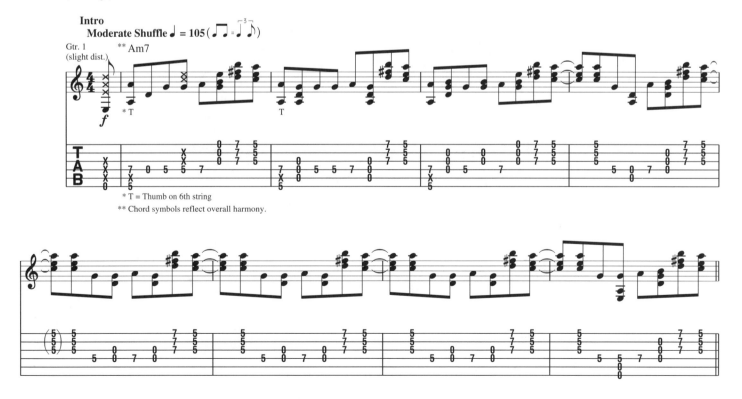

* T = Thumb on 6th string

** Chord symbols reflect overall harmony.

# Blackbird

### Words and Music by John Lennon and Paul McCartney

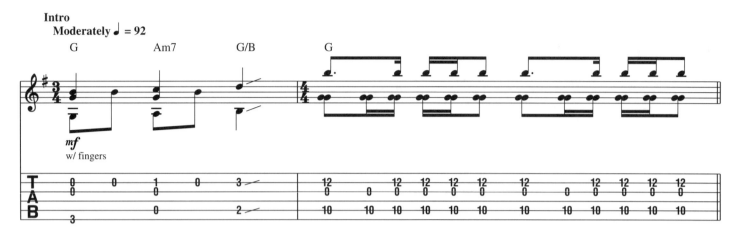

# Blue on Black

### Words and Music by Tia Sillers, Mark Selby and Kenny Wayne Shepherd

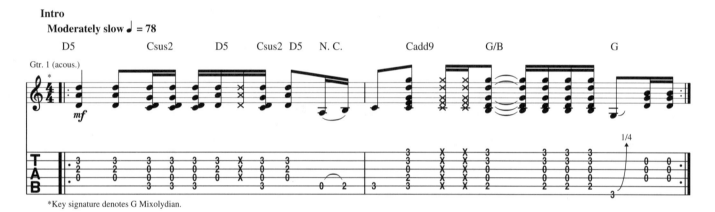

*Key signature denotes G Mixolydian.

# Blues With a Feeling

### Words and Music by Walter Jacobs

14

# Bombtrack

**Written and Arranged by Rage Against The Machine**

Intro

Moderately slow Rock ♩ = 80

Gtr. 1 (dist.)

# Boogie Chillen No. 2

**Words and Music by John Lee Hooker and Bernard Besman**

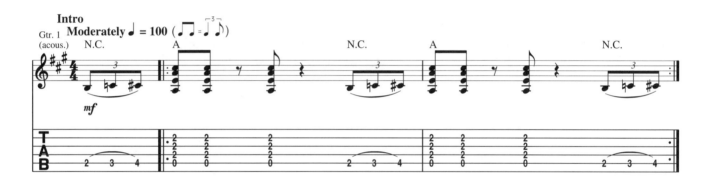

Intro

Gtr. 1 (acous.)  Moderately ♩ = 100

# Boom Boom

**Words and Music by John Lee Hooker**

Tune up 1/2 step:
(low to high) E#–A#–D#–G#–B#–E#

Intro

Moderate Shuffle

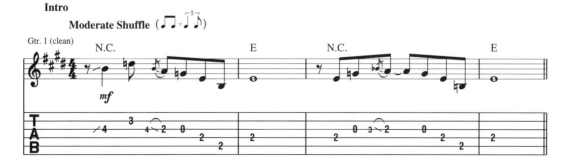

Gtr. 1 (clean)

# Break on Through to the Other Side

Words and Music by The Doors

# Burning for You

Words and Music by Donald Roeser and Richard Meltzer

# Call Me the Breeze

Words and Music by John Cale

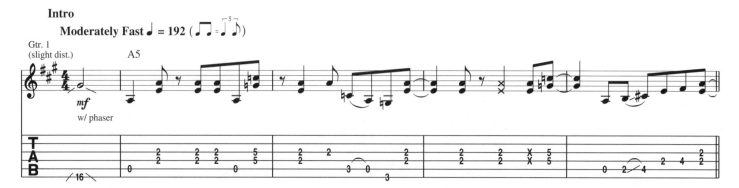

# Change the World

**Words and Music by Wayne Kirkpatrick, Gordon Kennedy and Tommy Sims**

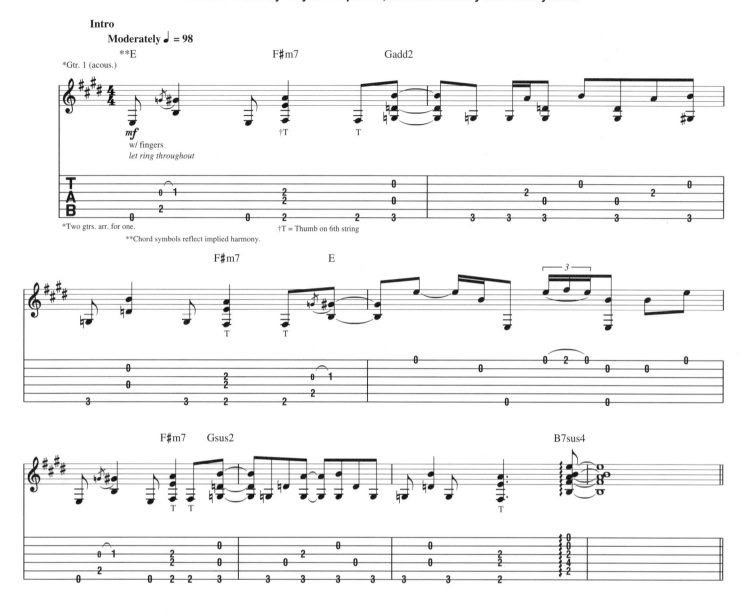

# Come Together

**Words and Music by John Lennon and Paul McCartney**

# Couldn't Stand the Weather

**Written by Stevie Ray Vaughan**

Tune down 1/2 step:
(low to high) Eb–Ab–Db–Gb–Bb–Eb

**Intro**

**Moderately** ♩ = 122

N.C.

Gtr. 1 (slight dist.)

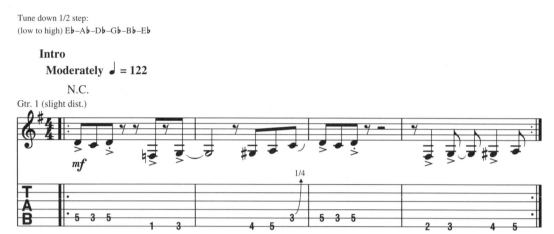

# Crazy Train

**Words and Music by Ozzy Osbourne, Randy Rhoads and Bob Daisley**

**Medium Rock** ♩ = 136

N.C.(F#5)          (D5)   (E5)   (F#5)                    (A5)          (E5)

Gtr. 1 (dist.)

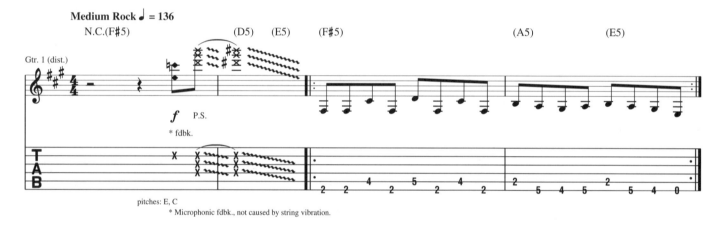

pitches: E, C

* Microphonic fdbk., not caused by string vibration.

# Crossfire

**Written by Bill Carter, Ruth Ellsworth, Reese Wynans, Tommy Shannon and Chris Layton**

Tune down 1/2 step:
(low to high) Eb–Ab–Db–Gb–Bb–Eb

**Intro**

**Moderate Rock** ♩ = 115

N.C.(E7)

Gtr. 1 (clean)

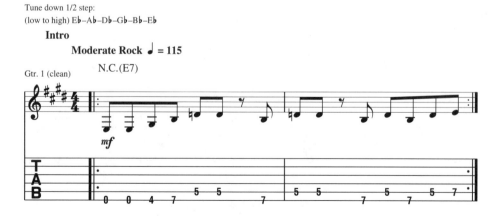

# Crash Into Me

**Words and Music by David J. Matthews**

Intro
Moderately ♩ = 102

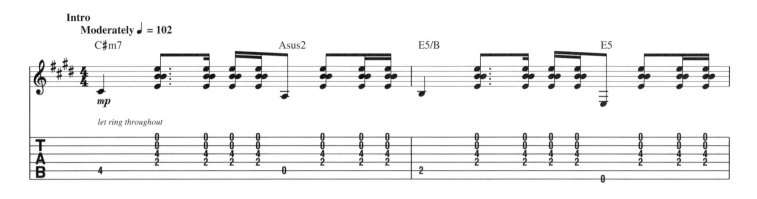

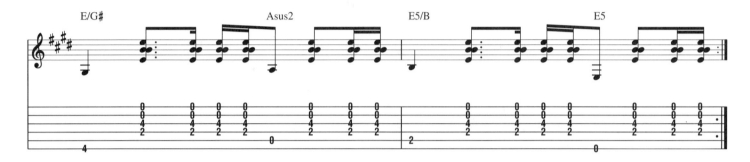

# Crushing Day

**Music by Joe Satriani**

Intro

Moderate Rock ♩ = 168

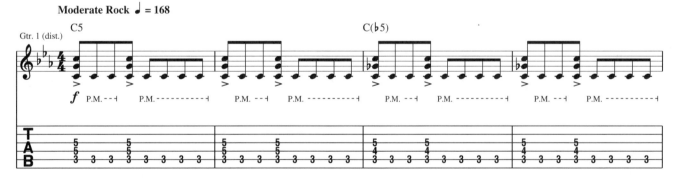

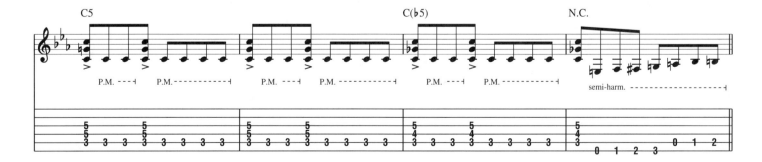

# Crazy on You

Words and Music by Ann Wilson, Nancy Wilson and Roger Fisher

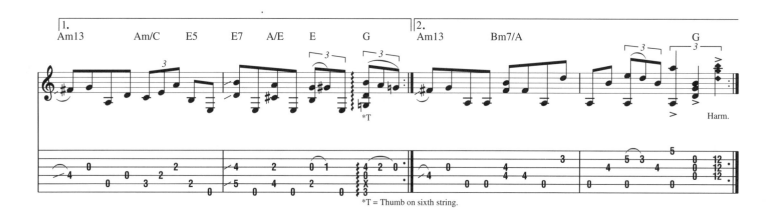

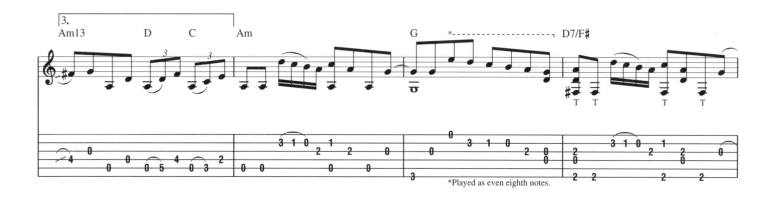

# Cult of Personality

**Words and Music by William Calhoun, Corey Glover, Muzz Skillings, and Vernon Reid**

# Day Tripper

**Words and Music by John Lennon and Paul McCartney**

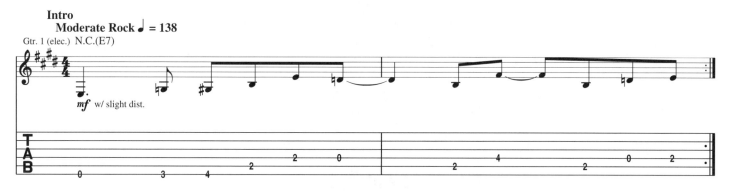

# De Do Do Do, De Da Da Da

**Written and Composed by Sting**

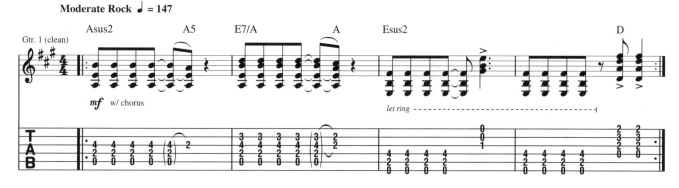

# Dear Prudence

**Words and Music by John Lennon and Paul McCartney**

Drop D tuning:
(low to high) D–A–D–G–B–E

### Intro

Moderately slow ♩ = 74

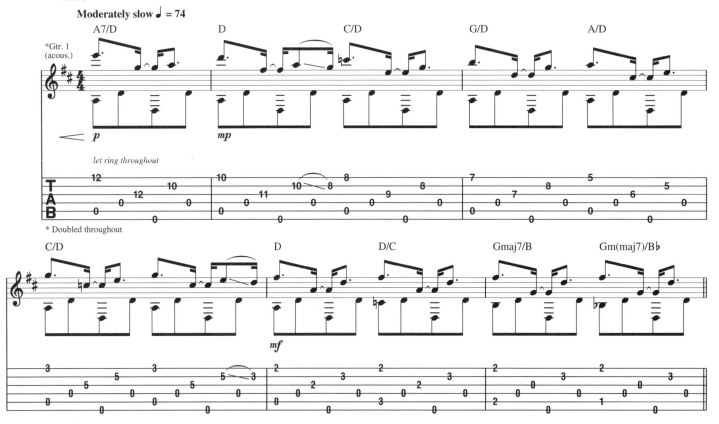

# Don't Treat Me Bad

**Words and Music by Bill Leverty, Carl Snare, Michael Foster and Cosby Ellis**

Tune down 1/2 step:
(low to high) Eb–Ab–Db–Gb–Bb–Eb

### Intro

Moderate Rock ♩ = 115

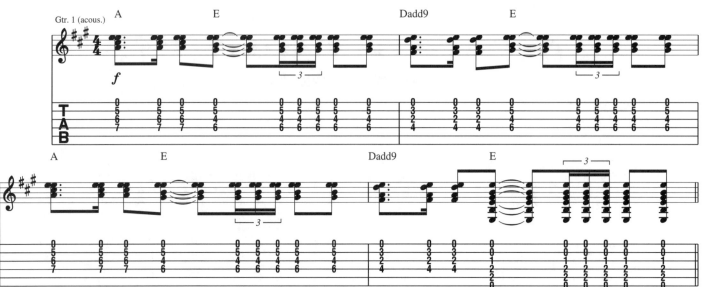

# The Distance

**Words and Music by Greg Brown**

**Chorus**
Moderately slow Rock ♩ = 94

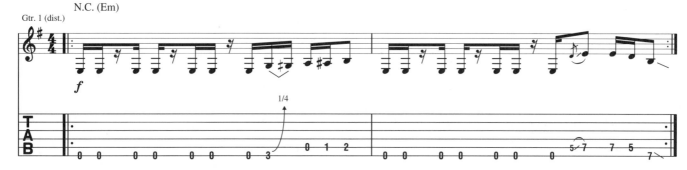

# Don't Fear the Reaper

**Words and Music by Donald Roeser**

Moderately ♩ = 138

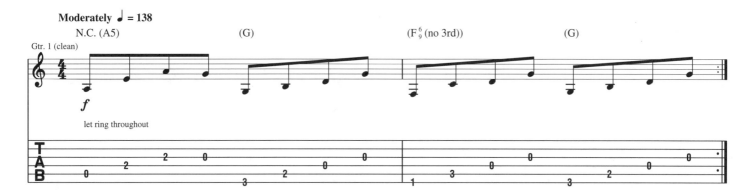

# Don't Let Me Be Misunderstood

**Words and Music by Bennie Benjamin, Sol Marcus and Gloria Caldwell**

**Intro**
Moderately Slow ♩ = 110

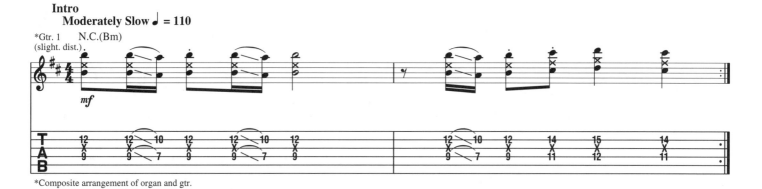

*Composite arrangement of organ and gtr.

# Eight Miles High

**Words and Music by Roger McGuinn, David Crosby and Gene Clark**

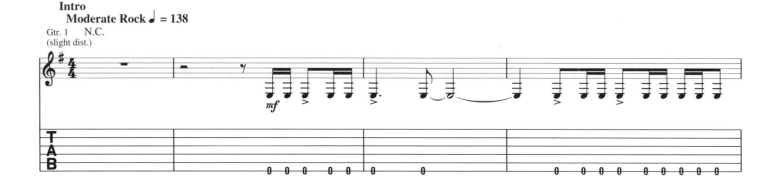

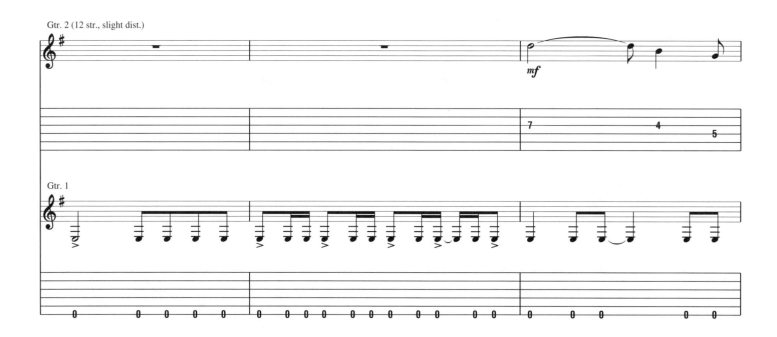

# Dream On

**Words and Music by Steven Tyler**

*Chord symbols reflect overall tonality.

# Every Breath You Take

### Written and Composed by Sting

Tune down 1/2 step:
(low to high) Eb–Ab–Db–Gb–Bb–Eb

**Intro**

**Moderate Rock** ♩ = 116

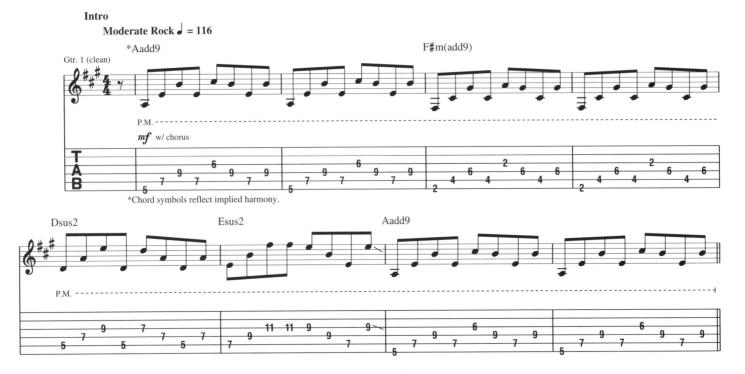

*Chord symbols reflect implied harmony.

# Fight for Your Right (To Party)

### Words and Music by Rick Rubin, Adam Horovitz and Adam Yauch

Tune down 1/2 step:
(low to high) Eb–Ab–Db–Gb–Bb–Eb

**Intro**

**Moderately** ♩ = 134

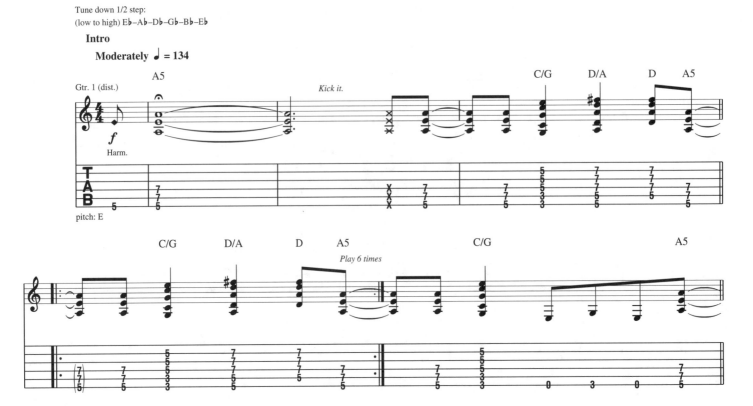

# 55th Street Boogie

**By Hound Dog Taylor**

# Fly

**Words and Music by Jonathan R. Mead, Bobby Stefano, Chris Hower and Kane McGee**

Drop D tuning, down 1/2 step:
(low to high) Db–Ab–Db–Gb–Bb–Eb

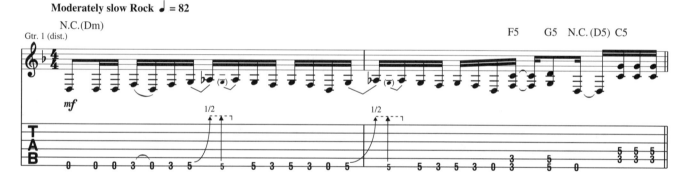

# Frankenstein

**By Edgar Winter**

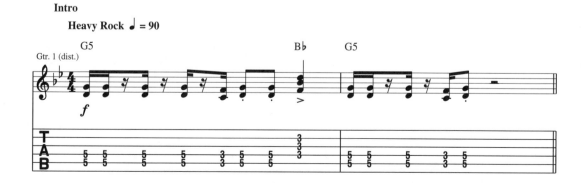

# Firehouse

**Words and Music by Paul Stanley**

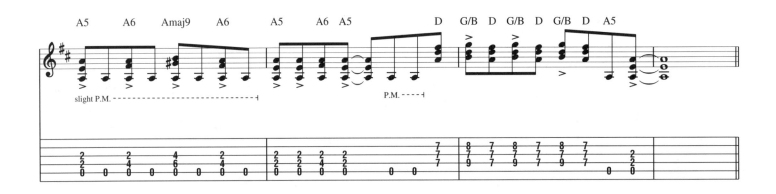

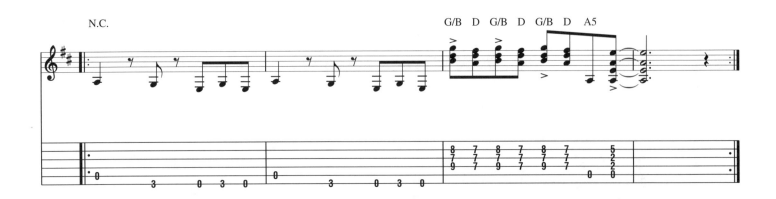

# Get the Funk Out

**Words and Music by Nuno Bettencourt and Gary Cherone**

Tune down 1/2 step:
(low to high) Eb–Ab–Db–Gb–Bb–Eb

# Gettin' Better

**Words and Music by Jeffrey Keith and Frank Hannon**

*Chord symbols reflect basic harmony.

# (Ghost) Riders in the Sky
## (A Cowboy Legend)

By Stan Jones

# Got You (Where I Want You)

**Lyrics by Adam Paskowitz**
**Music by The Flys**

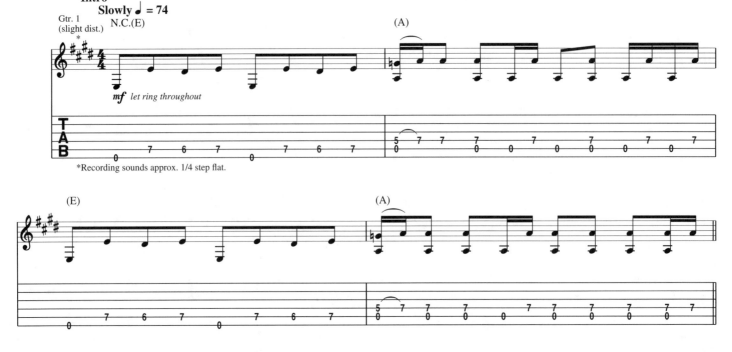

*Recording sounds approx. 1/4 step flat.

# Gloria

**Words and Music by Van Morrison**

Intro

Moderately fast ♩ = 130

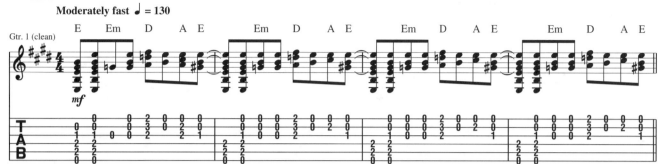

# Godzilla

**Words and Music by Donald Roeser**

Intro

Moderately ♩ = 90

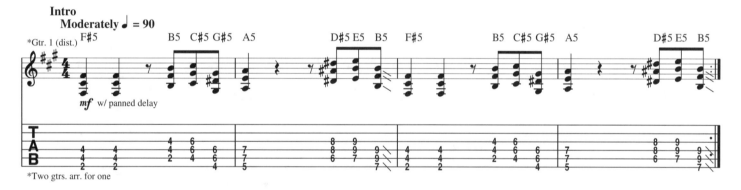

*Two gtrs. arr. for one

# Good Morning Little Schoolgirl

**Words and Music by Sonny Boy Williamson**

Moderately fast ♩ = 142

# Green Onions

**Written by Al Jackson, Jr., Lewis Steinberg, Booker T. Jones and Steve Cropper**

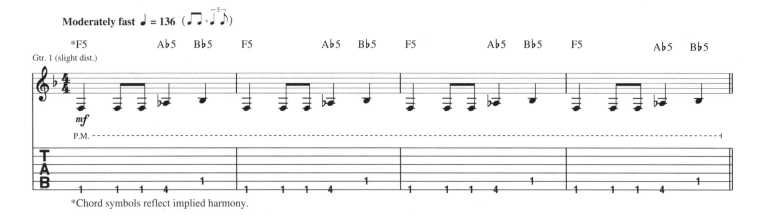

*Chord symbols reflect implied harmony.

# Hair of the Dog

**Words and Music by Dan McCafferty, Darrell Sweet, Pete Agnew and Manuel Charlton**

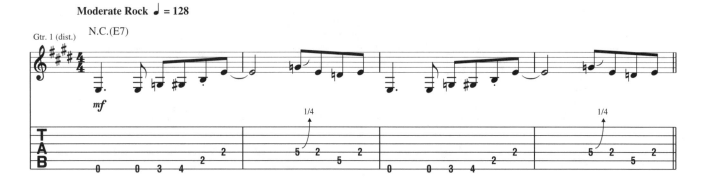

# Heart and Soul

**Words and Music by Mike Chapman and Nicky Chinn**

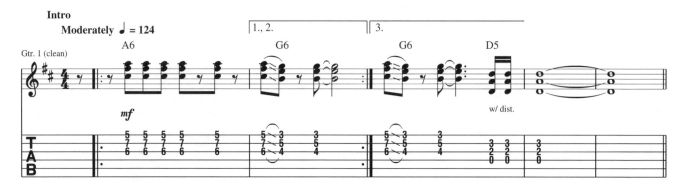

# A Hard Day's Night

Words and Music by John Lennon and Paul McCartney

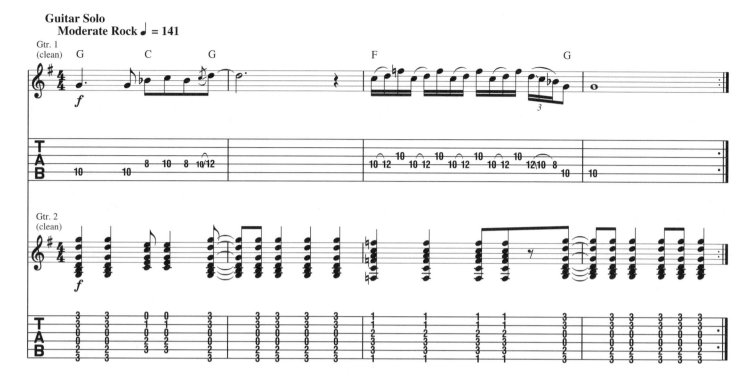

# Hope You're Feeling Better

Words and Music by Gregg Rolie

# Here Comes the Sun

**Words and Music by George Harrison**

Capo VII

**Intro**

Moderately fast ♩ = 144

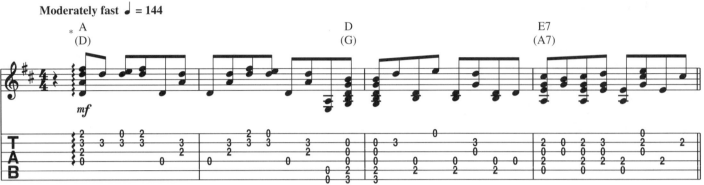

\* Symbols in parentheses represent chord names respective to capoed guitar.
Symbols above reflect actual sounding chords. Capoed fret is "O" in tab.

# Hey Bulldog

**Words and Music by John Lennon and Paul McCartney**

**Intro**

Gtr. 1
(dist.)   Moderate Rock ♩ = 105

# Hey Joe

**Words and Music by Billy Roberts**

**Intro**

Moderately Slow Rock ♩ = 82

Gtr. 1 (clean)

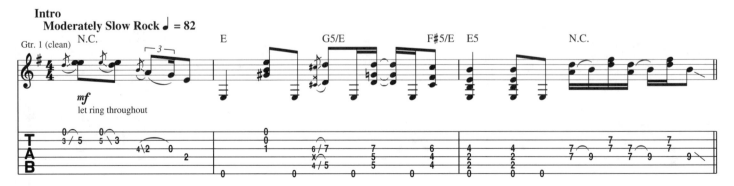

# Hide Away

**Words and Music by Freddie King and Sonny Thompson**

Intro

**Moderate Shuffle** ♩ = 144

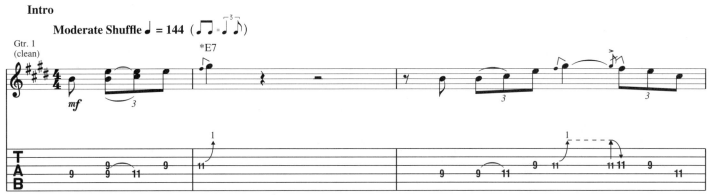

*Chord symbols reflect overall harmony.

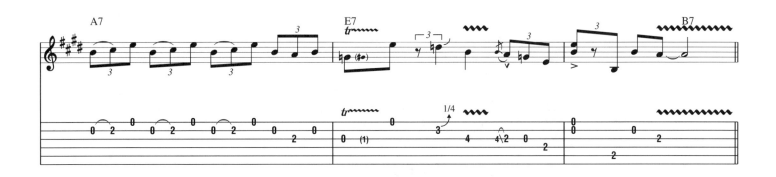

# Hit Me With Your Best Shot

**Words and Music by Eddie Schwartz**

Intro
Moderate Rock ♩ = 128

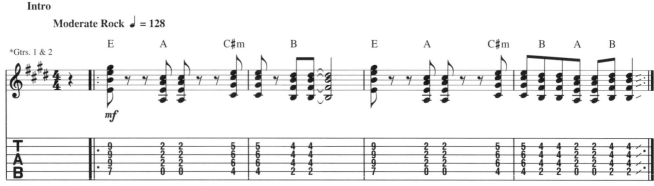

*Gtr. 1 (slight dist.); Gtr. 2 (clean)

# I Just Want to Make Love to You

**Written by Willie Dixon**

Intro
Moderate Rock ♩ = 128

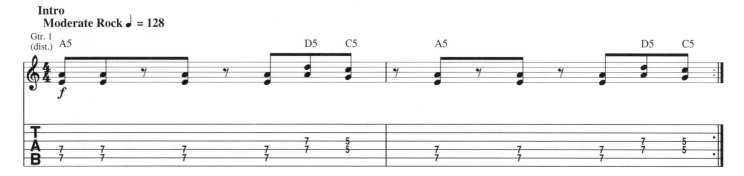

# I'm Your Hoochie Coochie Man

**Written by Willie Dixon**

Intro
Slow Blues ♩. = 50

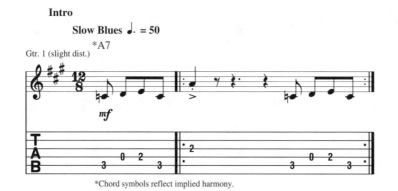

*Chord symbols reflect implied harmony.

# Hole Hearted

**Words and Music by Nuno Bettencourt and Gary Cherone**

Tune down 1/2 step:
(low to high) Eb–Ab–Db–Gb–Bb–Eb

**Intro**

**Moderate Rock** ♩ = 104

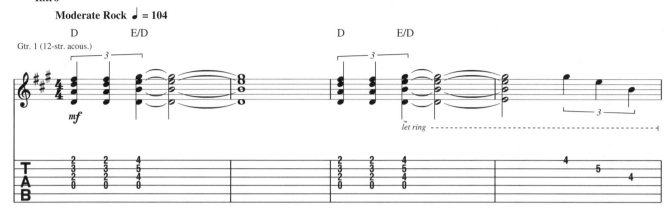

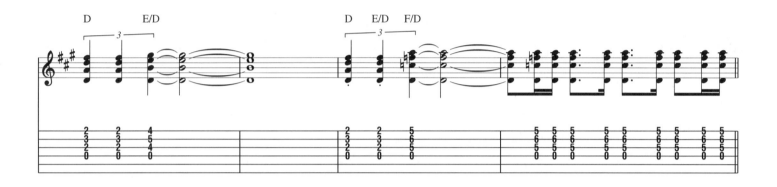

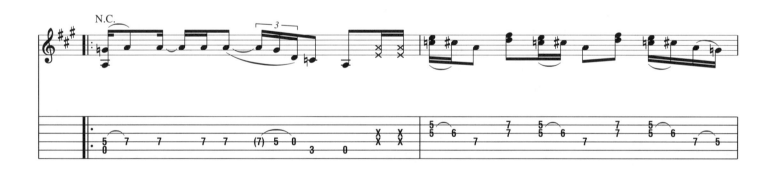

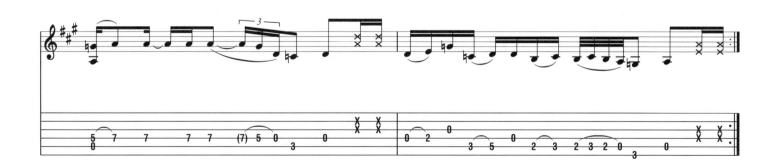

# How Many More Years

**Words and Music by Chester Burnett**

Verse

**Moderate Shuffle** ♩. = 110

# I Ain't Got You

By Calvin Carter

# I Can See for Miles

Words and Music by Peter Townshend

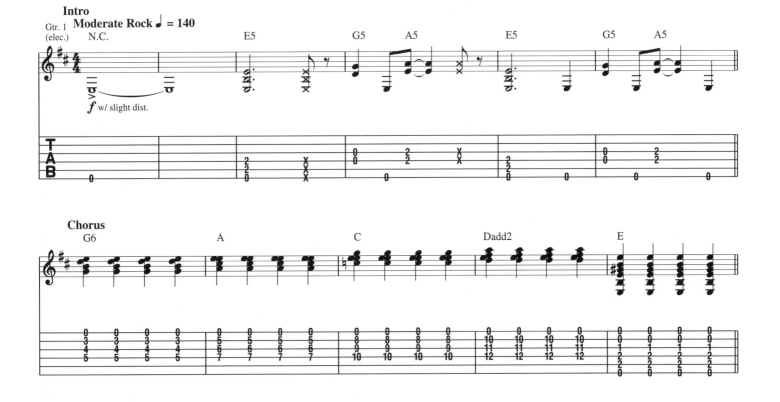

# I Feel Fine

Words and Music by John Lennon and Paul McCartney

*Chord symbols reflect implied tonality.

# Jack and Diane

Words and Music by John Mellencamp

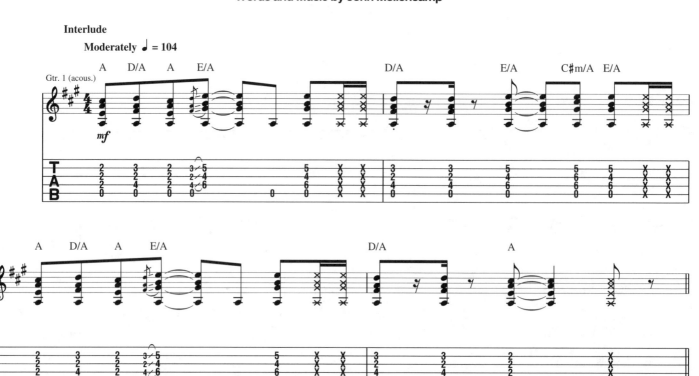

# I'm Tore Down

**Words and Music by Sonny Thompson**

Chorus
Moderate Blues ♩ = 134

*C7

Gtr. 1 (slight dist.)

*Chord symbols reflect basic harmony.

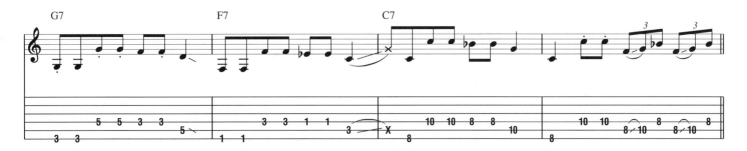

# Ice Cream Man

**Words and Music by John Brim**

Tune down 1/2 step:
(low to high) Eb–Ab–Db–Gb–Bb–Eb

**Intro**
Moderately fast Blues ♩ = 176

Gtr. 1 (acous.)

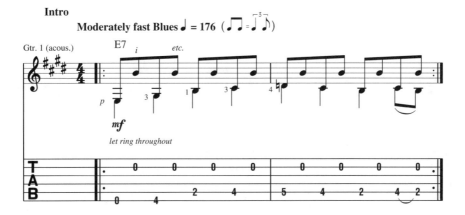

let ring throughout

# Ice Pick

### By Albert Collins

**Intro**
**Moderately** ♩ = 88

C7

Gtr. 1 (clean)

# Imagine

### Words and Music by John Lennon

**Intro**
**Slowly** ♩ = 78

*Gtr. 1  C                                    Cmaj7         F

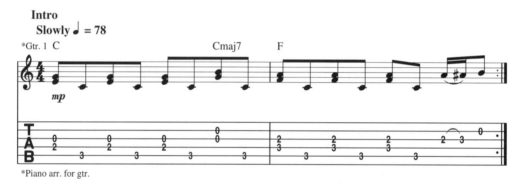

*Piano arr. for gtr.

# In and Out of Love

### Words and Music by Jon Bon Jovi

**Intro**
**Moderate Rock** ♩ = 128

A5

Gtr. 1 (dist.)

# In My Life

**Words and Music by John Lennon and Paul McCartney**

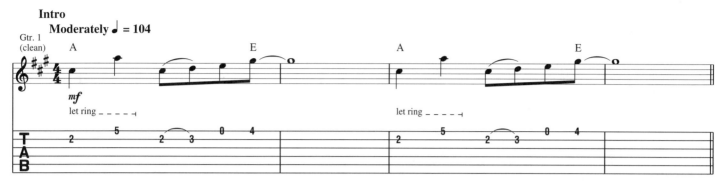

# Iron Man

**Words and Music by Frank Iommi, John Osbourne, William Ward and Terence Butler**

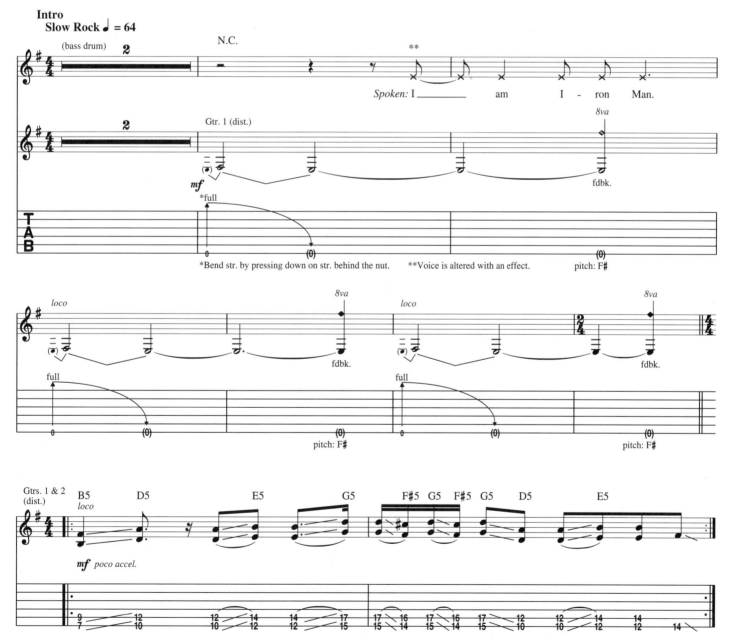

*Bend str. by pressing down on str. behind the nut.    **Voice is altered with an effect.*

# It's Only Love

**Words and Music by Bryan Adams and Jim Vallance**

# Jesus Is Just Alright

**Words and Music by Arthur Reynolds**

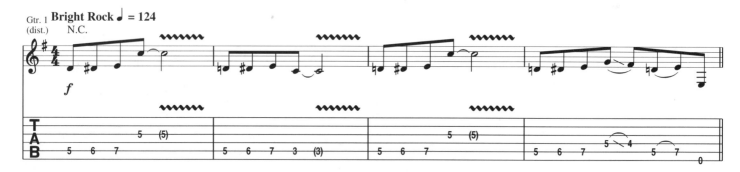

# Killing in the Name

**Written and Arranged by Rage Against The Machine**

Drop D tuning:
(low to high) D–A–D–G–B–E

**Intro**

# Killing Floor

**Words and Music by Chester Burnett**

## Intro
**Moderate Blues** ♩ = 120

*Chord symbols reflect overall harmony.

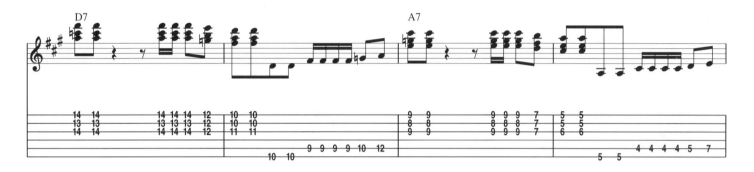

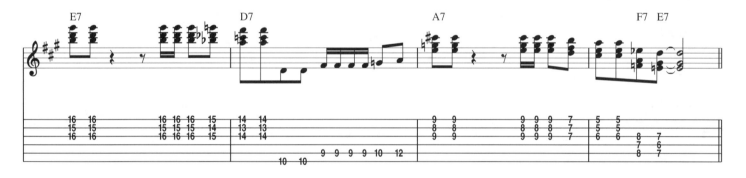

# La Bamba

**By Ritchie Valens**

## Intro
**Brightly** ♩ = 130

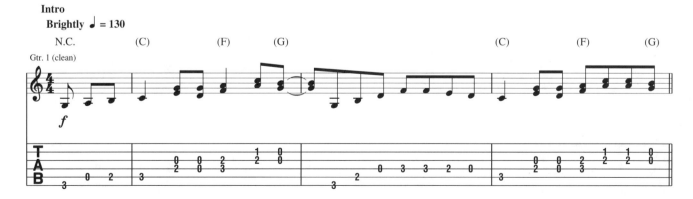

# Lady Madonna

**Words and Music by John Lennon and Paul McCartney**

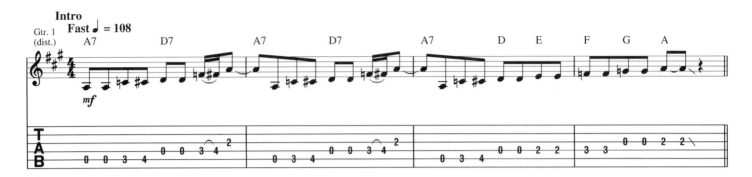

# Last Child

**Words and Music by Steven Tyler and Brad Whitford**

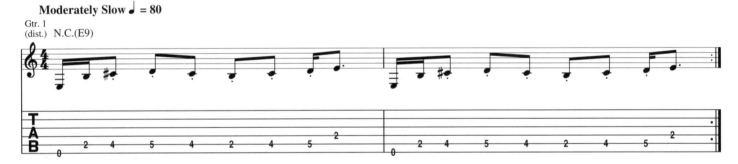

# Layla

**Words and Music by Eric Clapton and Jim Gordon**

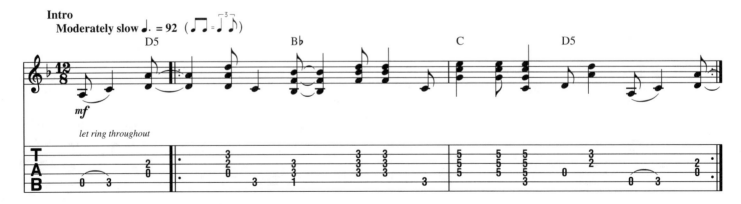

# Lay Down Sally

**Words and Music by Eric Clapton, Marcy Levy and George Terry**

# Little Sister

**Words and Music by Doc Pomus and Mort Shuman**

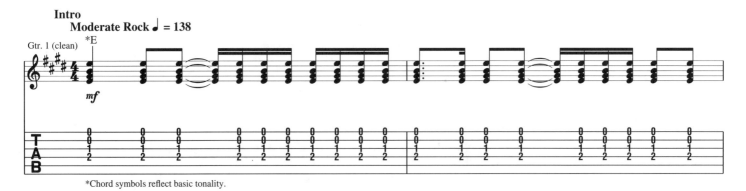

*Chord symbols reflect basic tonality.

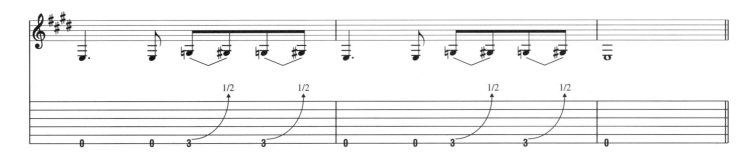

# Layla

**Words and Music by Eric Clapton and Jim Gordon**

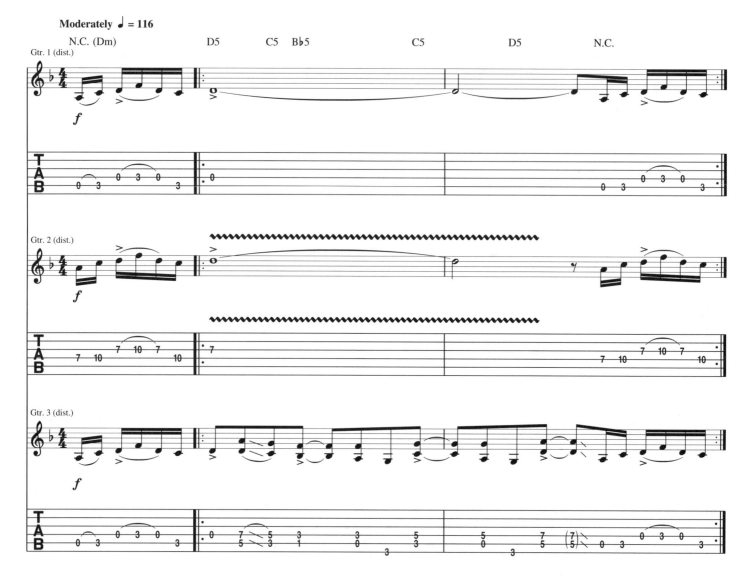

# Let Me Love You Baby

**Words and Music by Willie Dixon**

# Let's Live for Today

**Words and Music by Guido Cenciarelli, Giulio Rapetti and Norman David**

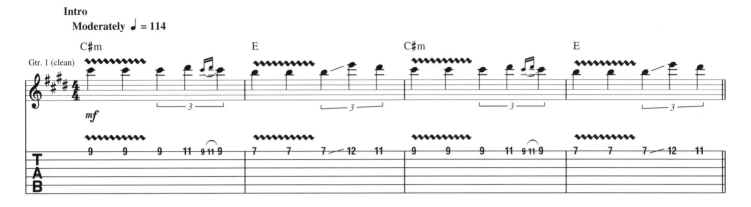

# Lit Up

**Words and Music by Joshua Todd Gruber, Keith Edward Nelson, Jonathan Brightman and Devon Glenn**

Open G tuning:
(low to high) D–G–D–G–B–D

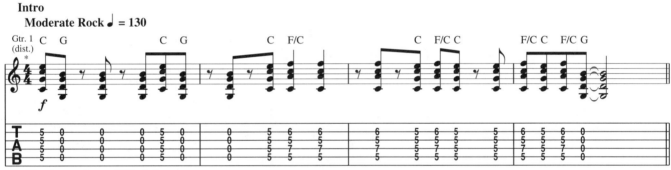

*Key signature denotes G Mixolydian.

# Little Red Rooster

**Written by Willie Dixon**

Open G tuning:
(low to high) D–G–D–G–B–D

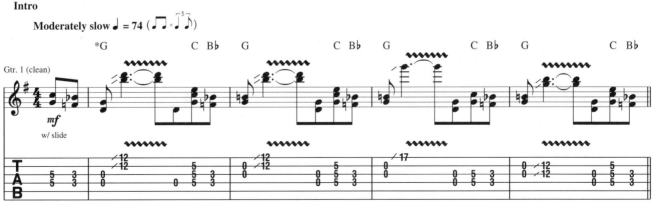

*Chord symbols reflect basic harmony.

# Long Cool Woman (In a Black Dress)

**Words and Music by Allan Clarke, Roger Cook and Roger Greenaway**

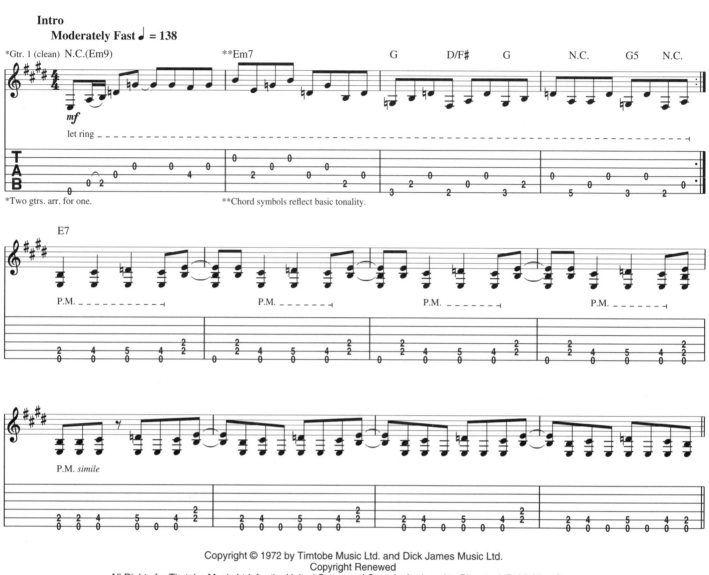

*Two gtrs. arr. for one.    **Chord symbols reflect basic tonality.

# Loser

**Words by Beck Hansen**

**Music by Beck Hansen and Karl Stephenson**

Drop D tuning:
(low to high) D–A–D–G–B–E

# Love Song

Words and Music by Jeffrey Keith and Frank Hannon

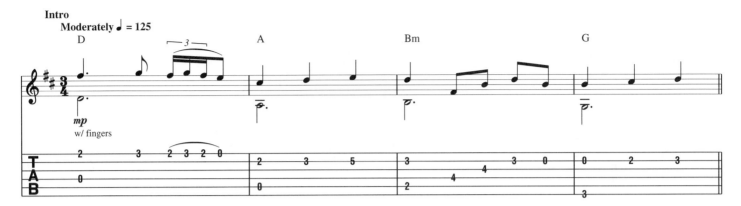

# Mannish Boy

Words and Music by McKinley Morganfield (Muddy Waters), M.R. London and Ellas McDaniel

*Chord symbols reflect overall harmony.

# Message in a Bottle

Written and Composed by Sting

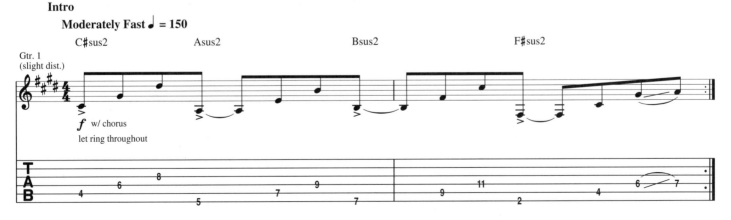

# The Magic Bus

**Words and Music by Peter Townshend**

**Intro**
**Moderately fast** ♩ = 195

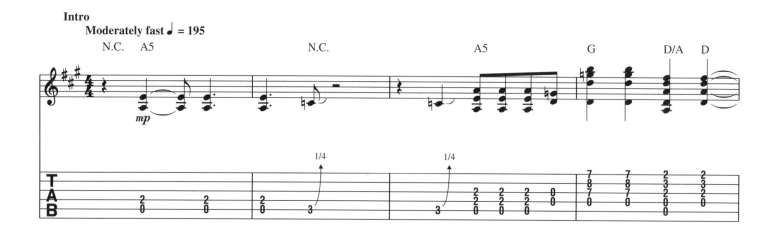

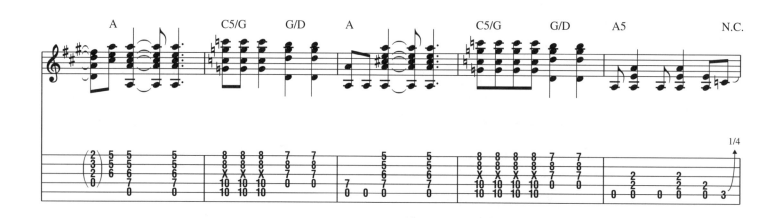

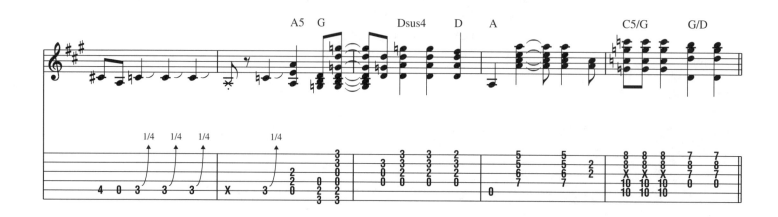

# Man in the Box

**Written by Jerry Cantrell and Layne Staley**

Tune down 1/2 step:
(low to high) Eb–Ab–Db–Gb–Bb–Eb

**Moderate Rock** ♩ = 108

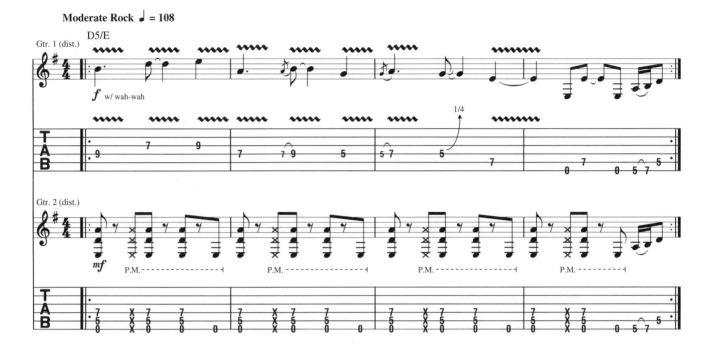

# Money for Nothing

**Words and Music by Mark Knopfler and Sting**

**Intro**
**Moderate Rock** ♩ = 135

Pitch: D

# Mary Had a Little Lamb

**Written by Buddy Guy**

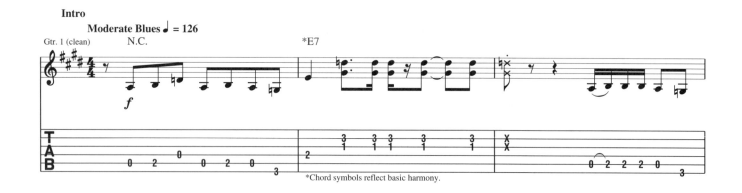

*Chord symbols reflect basic harmony.

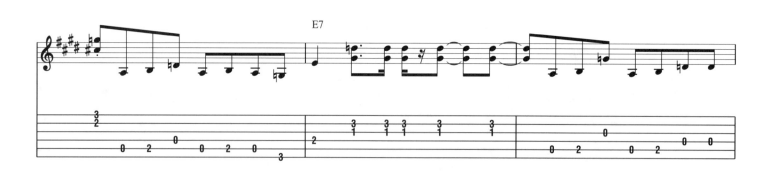

# Michelle

**Words and Music by John Lennon and Paul McCartney**

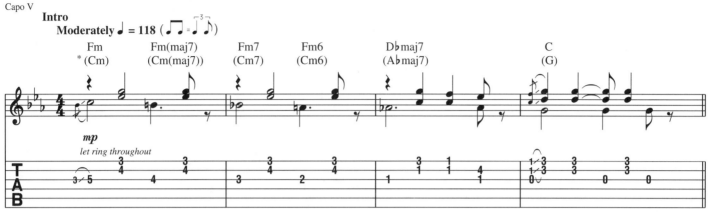

* Symbols in parentheses represent chord names respective to capoed guitar.
  Symbols above reflect actual sounding chords. Capoed fret is "0" in tab.

# More Than Words

**Words and Music by Nuno Bettencourt and Gary Cherone**

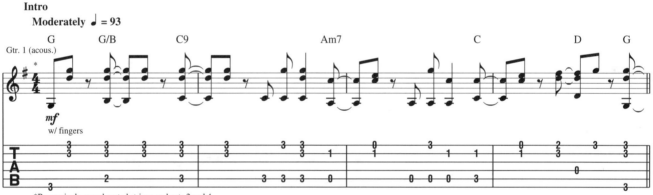

*Percussively sound muted strings on beats 2 and 4
of each measure with all four fingers of the right hand.

# No Excuses

**Written by Jerry Cantrell**

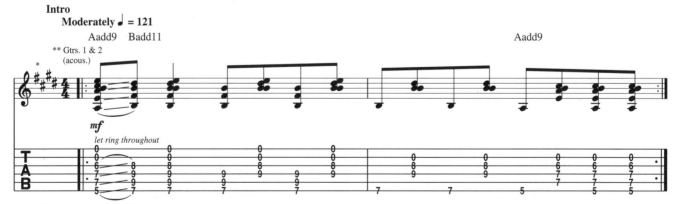

* Key signature denotes B Mixolydian.

** Composite arrangement

# Mississippi Queen

**Words and Music by Leslie West, Felix Pappalardi, Corky Laing and David Rea**

# My Sweet Lord

**Words and Music by George Harrison**

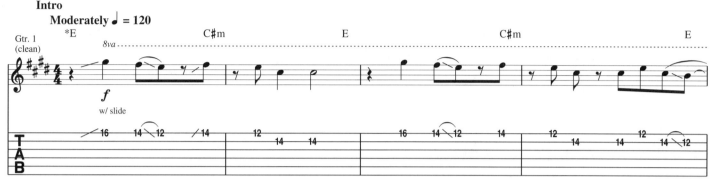

*Chord symbols reflect overall tonality.

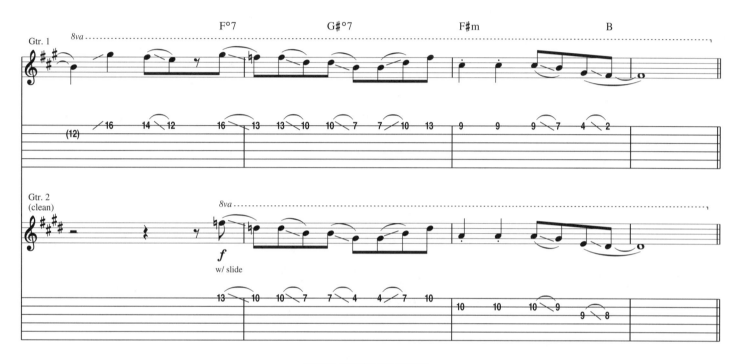

# Outshined

**Words and Music by Chris Cornell**

Drop D tuning:
(low to high) D–A–D–G–B–E

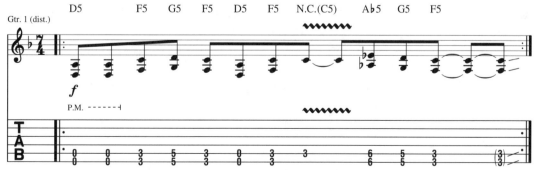

# No Particular Place to Go

**Words and Music by Chuck Berry**

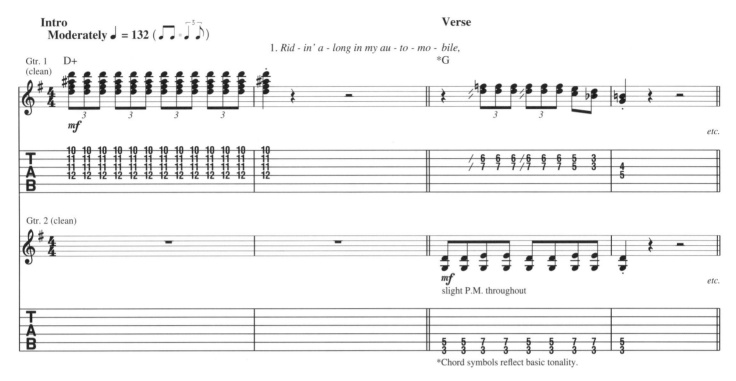

*Chord symbols reflect basic tonality.

# Norwegian Wood
## (This Bird Has Flown)

**Words and Music by John Lennon and Paul McCartney**

* Symbols in parentheses represent chord names respective to capoed guitar. Symbols above reflect actual sounding chords. Capoed fret is "0" in tab.

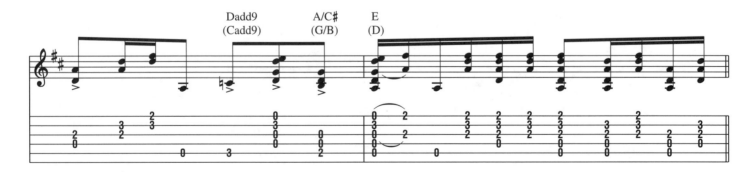

# Not Fade Away

**Words and Music by Charles Hardin and Norman Petty**

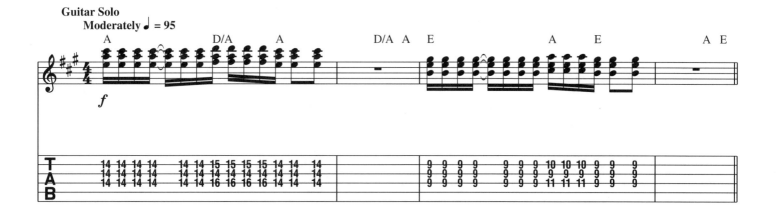

# Paperback Writer

**Words and Music by John Lennon and Paul McCartney**

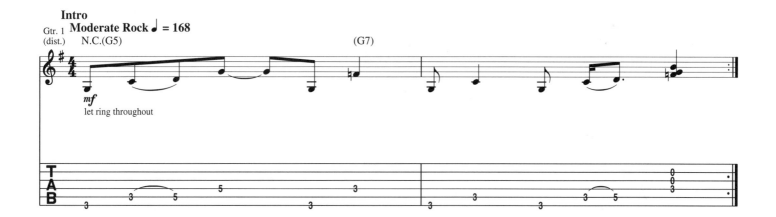

# Paranoid

**Words and Music by Anthony Iommi, John Osbourne,
William Ward and Terence Butler**

Fast Rock ♩ = 164

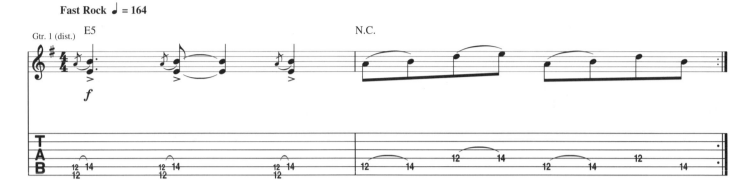

# Pink Houses

**Words and Music by John Mellencamp**

Open G tuning:
(low to high) D–G–D–G–B–D

### Intro

Moderately ♩ = 114

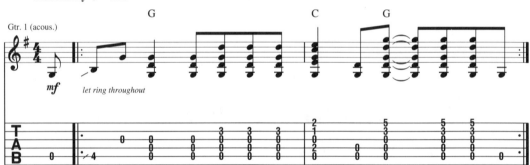

# Refugee

**Words and Music by Tom Petty and Mike Campbell**

### Intro

Moderate Rock ♩ = 116

# Pride and Joy

**Written by Stevie Ray Vaughan**

Tune down 1/2 step:
(low to high) Eb–Ab–Db–Gb–Bb–Eb

**Intro**

Moderate Shuffle ♩ = 122

# Round and Round

**Words and Music by Robbin Lantz Crosby, Warren DeMartini and Stephen E. Pearcy**

Tune down 1/2 step:
(low to high) Eb–Ab–Db–Gb–Bb–Eb

**Intro**

Moderate Rock ♩ = 128

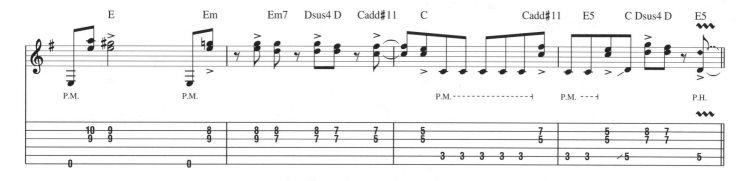

# Rest in Peace

**Words and Music by Nuno Bettencourt and Gary Cherone**

Tune down 1/2 step:
(low to high) Eb–Ab–Db–Gb–Bb–Eb

**Intro**

Moderately ♩ = 104

N.C.

Gtr. 1 (dist.)

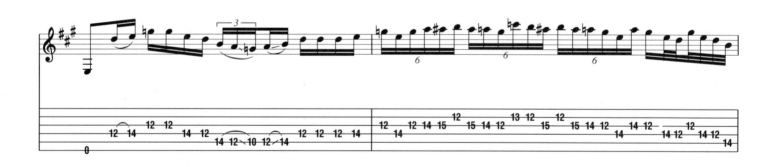

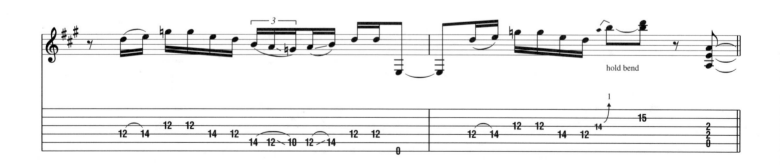

# Rock and Roll All Nite

**Words and Music by Paul Stanley and Gene Simmons**

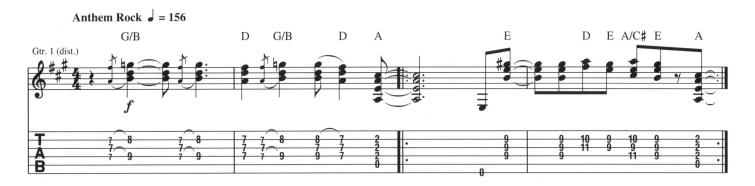

# Rock and Roll Hoochie Koo

**Words and Music by Rick Derringer**

# Rock You Like a Hurricane

**Words and Music by Herman Rarebell, Klaus Meine and Rudolf Schenker**

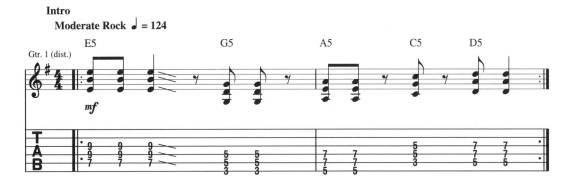

# Rock Me Baby

**Words and Music by B.B. King and Joe Bihari**

Intro

Moderately slow ♩ = 89

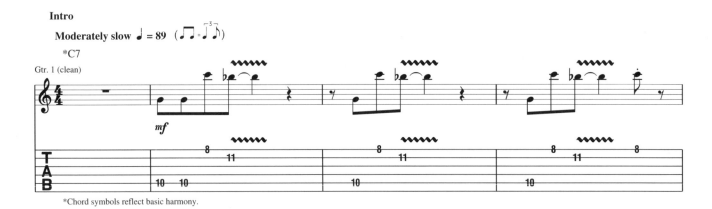

*Chord symbols reflect basic harmony.

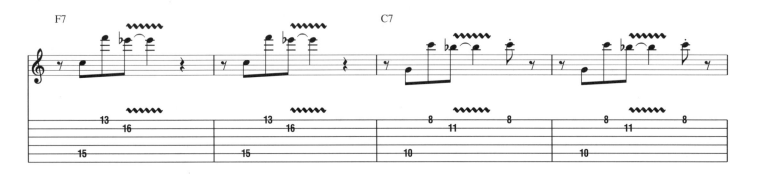

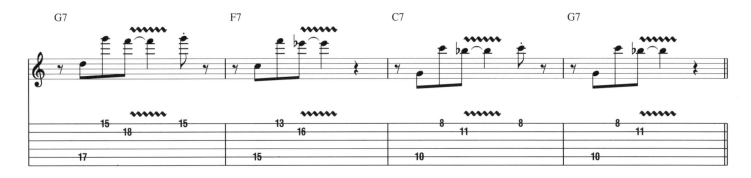

# Rollin' Stone
## (Catfish Blues)

**Written by McKinley Morganfield (Muddy Waters)**

Slow Blues ♩ = 88

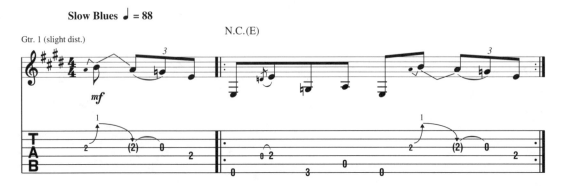

# Rocket '88

### Words and Music by Jackie Brenston

Tune down 1/2 step:
(low to high) Eb–Ab–Db–Gb–Bb–Eb

\* Chord symbols reflect basic harmony.

# Run Run Run

### Words and Music by Peter Townshend

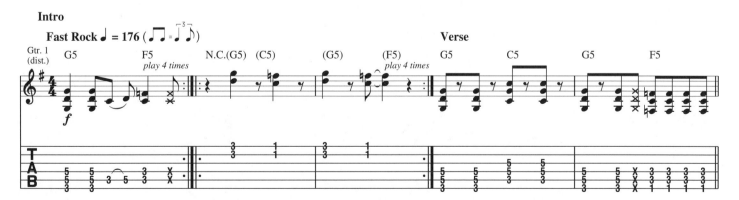

# Roxanne

**Written and Composed by Sting**

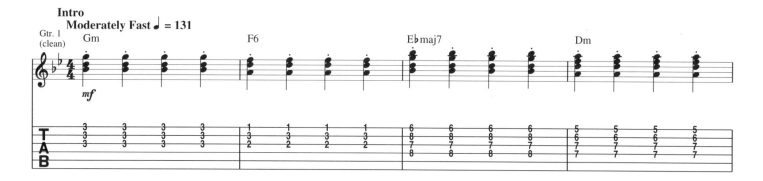

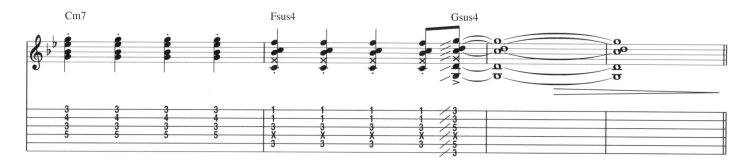

# Scuttle Buttin'

**Written by Stevie Ray Vaughan**

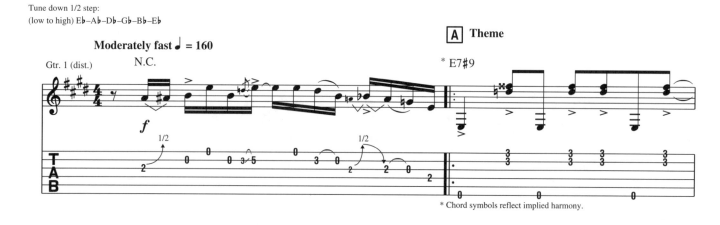

* Chord symbols reflect implied harmony.

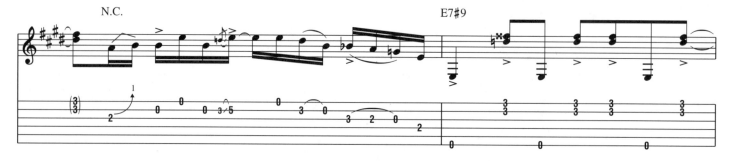

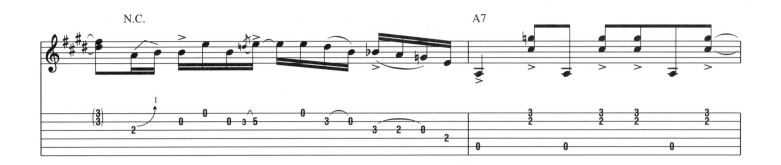

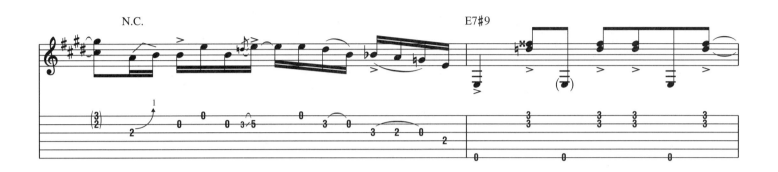

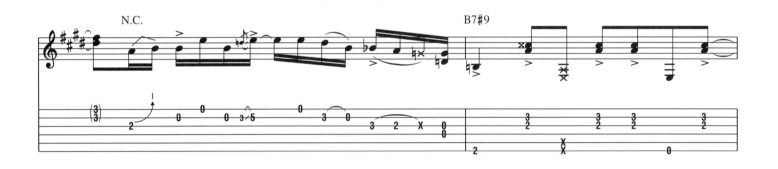

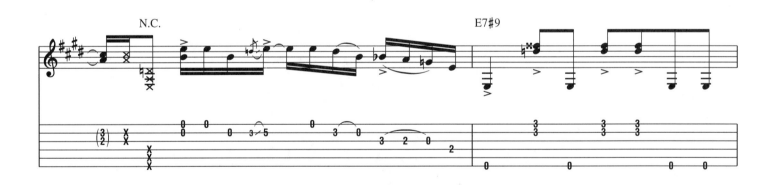

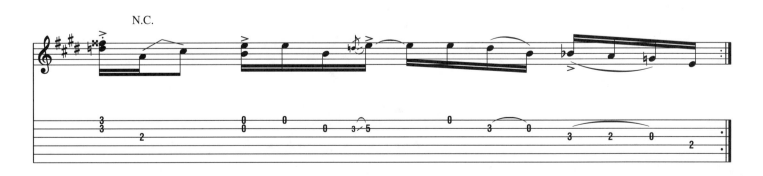

# Run to You

**Words and Music by Bryan Adams and Jim Vallance**

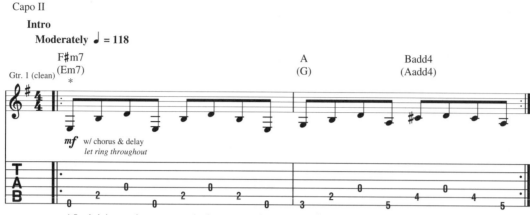

* Symbols in parentheses represent chord names respective to capoed guitar.
  Symbols above reflect actual sounding chords. Capoed fret is "O" in tab.
  Chord symbols reflect implied harmony.

# Run Around

**Words and Music by John Popper**

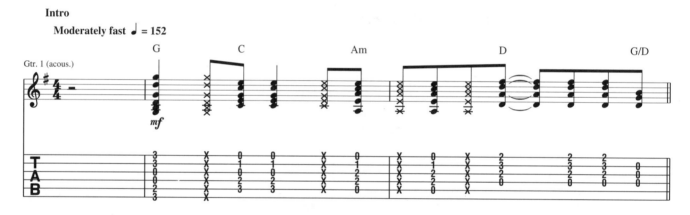

# Same Old Song & Dance

**Words and Music by Steven Tyler and Joe Perry**

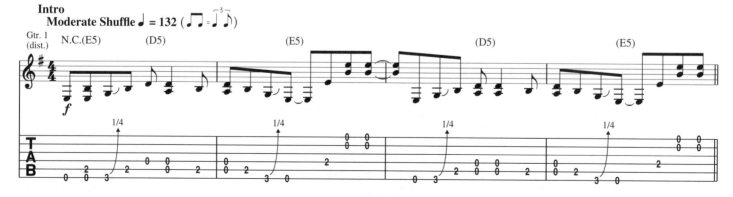

# Satch Boogie

By Joe Satriani

# Satellite

Words and Music by David J. Matthews

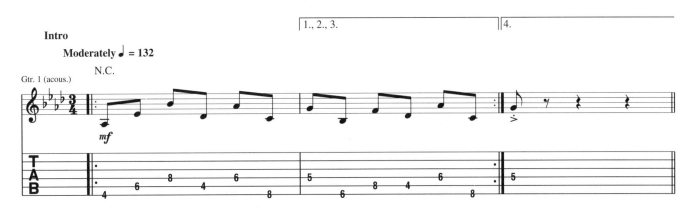

# Satisfy Susie

Words and Music by Lonnie McIntosh and Tim Drummond

† Tune down 1 step, Capo III:
(low to high) D–G–C–F–A–D

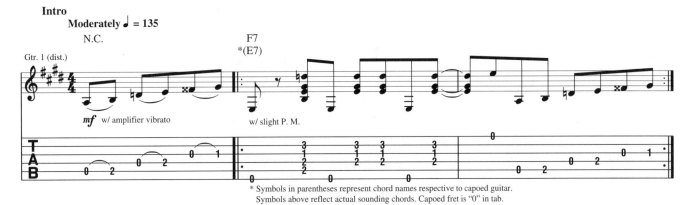

\* Symbols in parentheses represent chord names respective to capoed guitar.
Symbols above reflect actual sounding chords. Capoed fret is "0" in tab.

† Editor's note: You can accomplish the same result without tuning down a whole step by remaining in standard tuning and capoing at the first fret.

# School's Out

**Words and Music by Alice Cooper, Neal Smith, Michael Bruce, Glen Buxton and Dennis Dunaway**

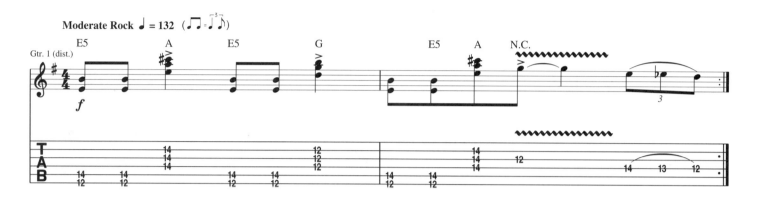

# Sgt. Pepper's Lonely Hearts Club Band

**Words and Music by John Lennon and Paul McCartney**

# Show Me the Way

**Words and Music by Peter Frampton**

Open G tuning:
(low to high) D–G–D–G–B–D

**Intro**

Moderately ♩ = 134

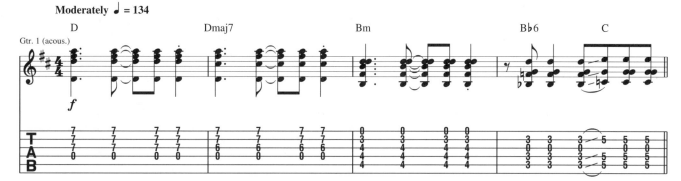

# Smokestack Lightning

**Words and Music by Chester Burnett**

**Intro**

Moderately ♩ = 144

# Spoonman

**Words and Music by Chris Cornell**

Drop D tuning:
(low to high) D–A–D–G–B–E

Moderately slow Rock ♩ = 98

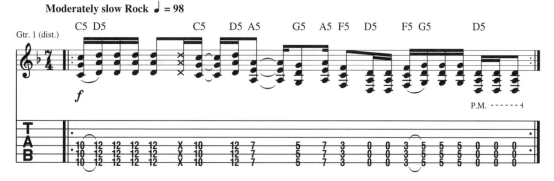

# Space Oddity

**Words and Music by David Bowie**

**Intro**
**Slowly** ♩ = 68

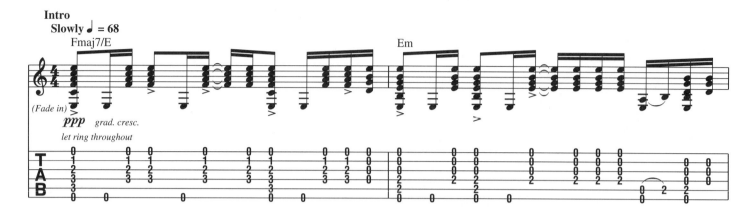

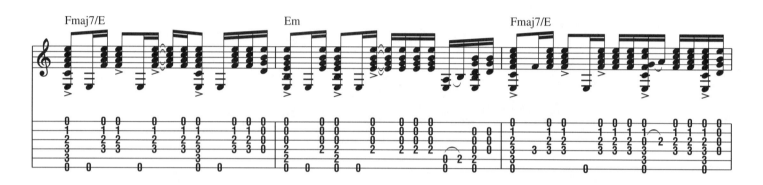

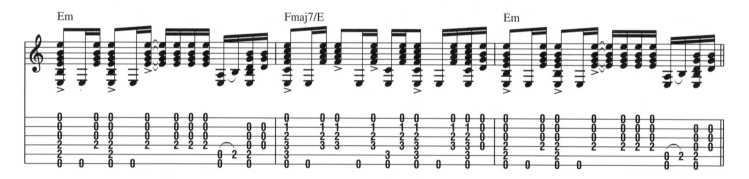

# Statesboro Blues

**Words and Music by Willy McTell**

**Intro**
**Moderately** ♩ = 125

N.C.          (D)

Gtr. 1 (slight dist.)

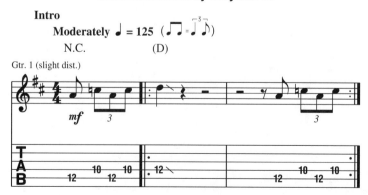

# Stayin' Alive

### from the Motion Picture SATURDAY NIGHT FEVER
**Words and Music by Barry Gibb, Maurice Gibb and Robin Gibb**

# Still a Fool

**Written by McKinley Morganfield (Muddy Waters)**

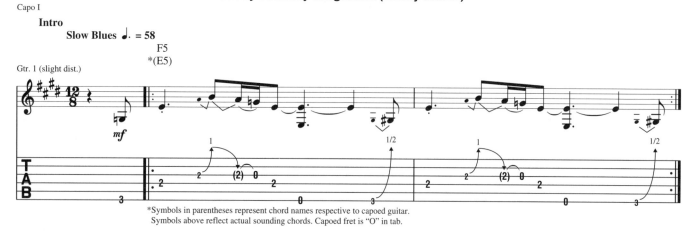

*Symbols in parentheses represent chord names respective to capoed guitar.
Symbols above reflect actual sounding chords. Capoed fret is "O" in tab.

# The Story in Your Eyes

**Words and Music by Justin Hayward**

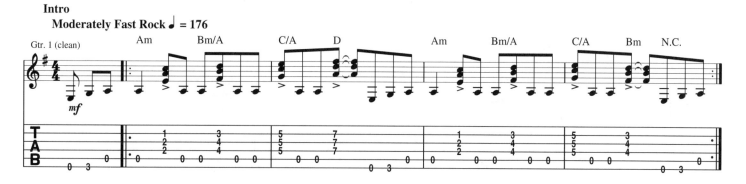

# Substitute

**Words and Music by Peter Townshend**

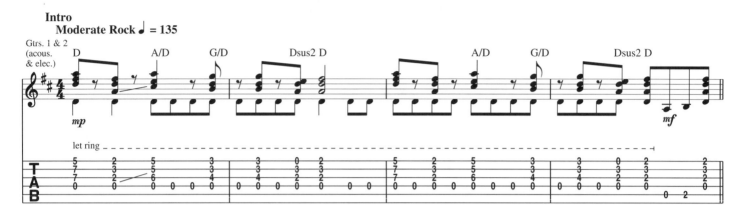

# Sugar

**Words and Music by Daron Malakian, Serj Tankian, Shavo Odadjian and John Dolmayan**

Drop D tuning, down 1 step:
(low to high) C–G–C–F–A–D

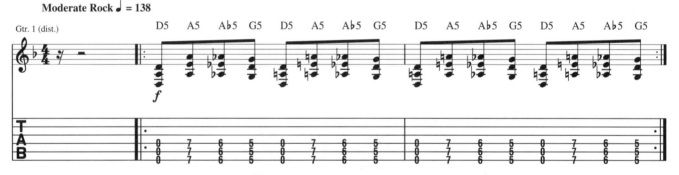

# Sunshine of Your Love

**Words and Music by Jack Bruce, Pete Brown and Eric Clapton**

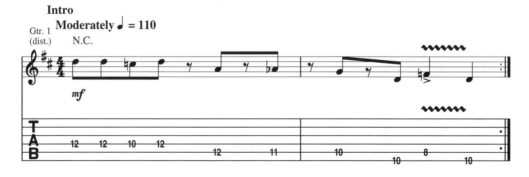

# Suite: Judy Blue Eyes

**Words and Music by Stephen Stills**

Gtr. 1 tuning:
(low to high) E–E↓–E–E–B–E

**Intro**
**Moderately** ♩ = 140

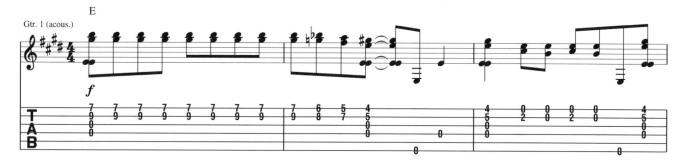

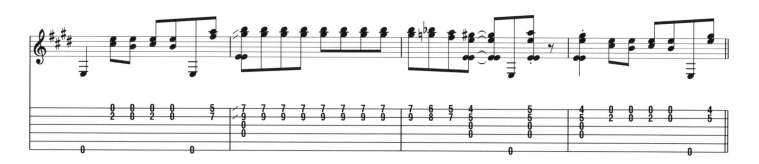

# Sultans of Swing

**Words and Music by Mark Knopfler**

**Intro**
**Moderately** ♩ = 146

Gtr. 1 (clean)

# Susie-Q

**Words and Music by Dale Hawkins, Stan Lewis and Eleanor Broadwater**

Intro
Moderate Rock ♩ = 126

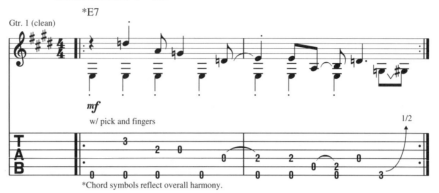

*Chord symbols reflect overall harmony.

# Sweet Emotion

**Words and Music by Steven Tyler and Tom Hamilton**

Interlude
Moderate Rock ♩ = 96

# Sweet Leaf

**Words and Music by Frank Iommi, John Osbourne, William Ward and Terence Butler**

Intro
Heavy Rock ♩ = 75

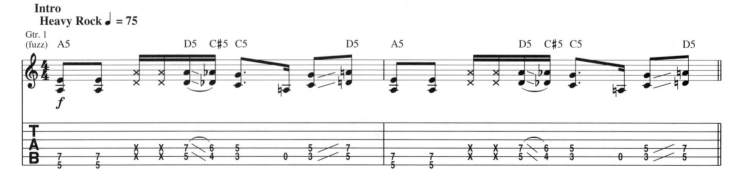

# Suzi
## (Wants Her All Day What?)

**Words and Music by Nuno Bettencourt and Gary Cherone**

Tune down 1/2 step:
(low to high) Eb–Ab–Db–Gb–Bb–Eb

**Moderately** ♩ = 120

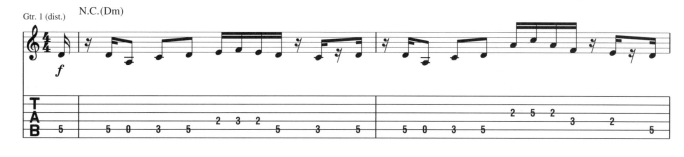

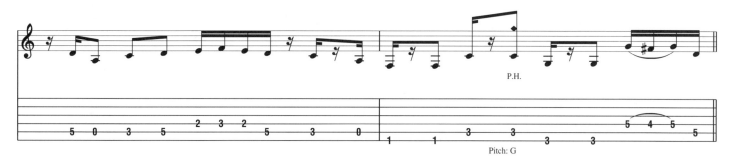

# Takin' Care of Business

**Words and Music by Randy Bachman**

**Intro**

**Fast Rock** ♩ = 132

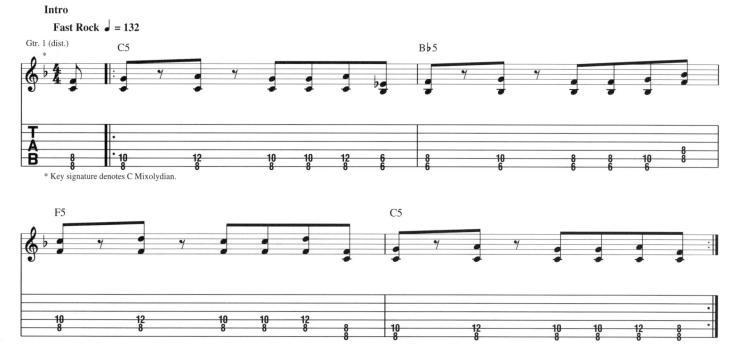

* Key signature denotes C Mixolydian.

# Tears in Heaven

**Words and Music by Eric Clapton and Will Jennings**

# Time for Me to Fly

**Words and Music by Kevin Cronin**

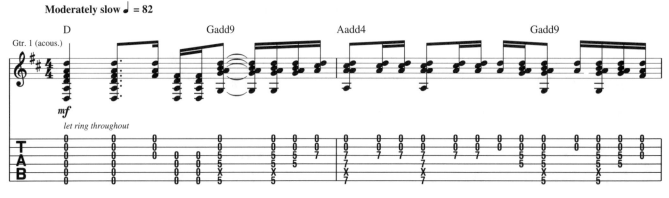

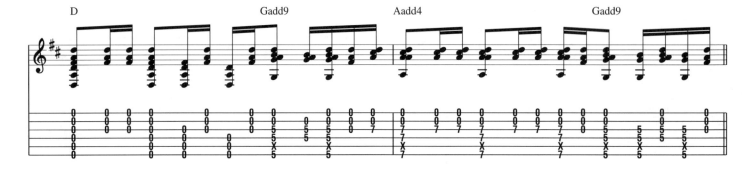

# That'll Be the Day

**Words and Music by Jerry Allison, Norman Petty and Buddy Holly**

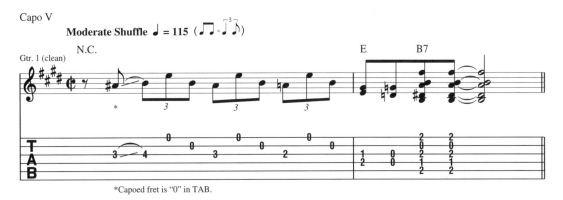

*Capoed fret is "0" in TAB.

# Them Bones

**Written by Jerry Cantrell**

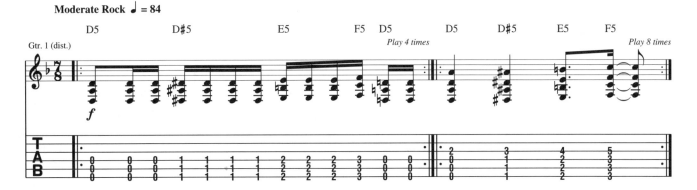

# Ticket to Ride

**Words and Music by John Lennon and Paul McCartney**

# Time in a Bottle

**Words and Music by Jim Croce**

*Symbols in parentheses represent chord names respective to capoed guitar.
Symbols above reflect actual sounding chords. Capoed fret is "0" in tab.

# Tuff Enuff

**Words and Music by Kim Wilson**

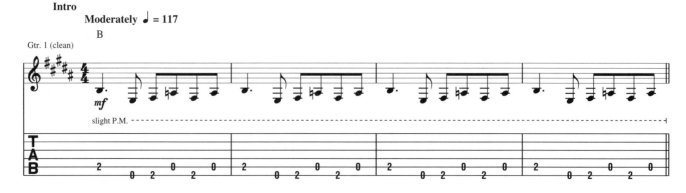

# Turn! Turn! Turn!
## (To Everything There Is a Season)

**Words from the Book of Ecclesiastes**
**Adaptation and Music by Pete Seeger**

Gtr. 1; Drop D Tuning:
① = E   ④ = D
② = B   ⑤ = A
③ = G   ⑥ = D

**Intro**
**Moderate Folk-Rock** ♩ = 120

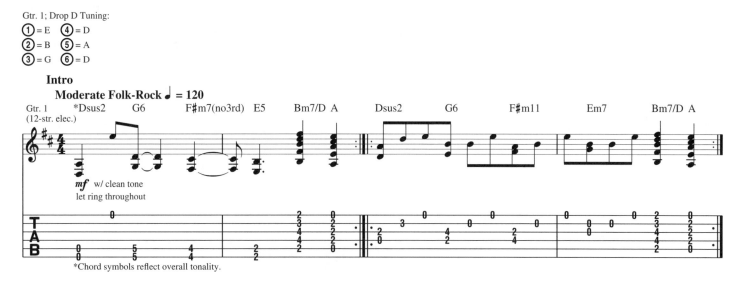

*Chord symbols reflect overall tonality.

# Twist and Shout

**Words and Music by Bert Russell and Phil Medley**

**Intro**
**Moderate Rock** ♩ = 122

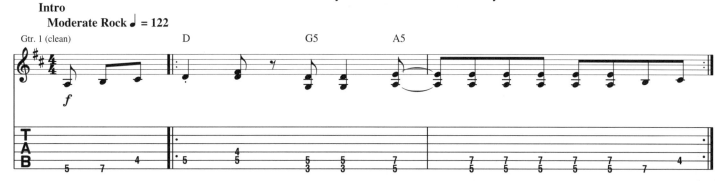

# Two Princes

**Words and Music by Spin Doctors**

**Moderate Rock** ♩ = 108

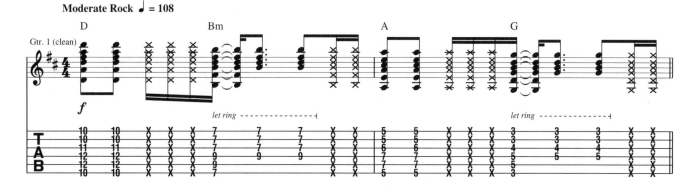

# Wake Up Little Susie

**Words and Music by Boudleaux Bryant and Felice Bryant**

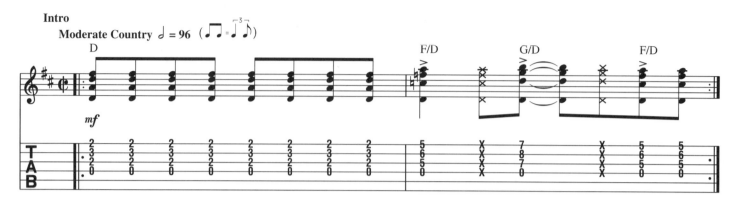

# Walk Don't Run

**By Johnny Smith**

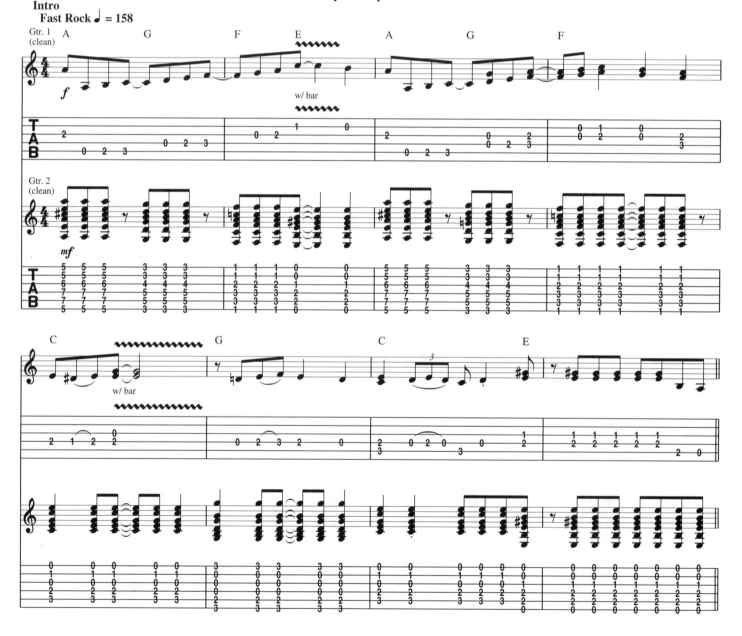

# Walk This Way

**Words and Music by Steven Tyler and Joe Perry**

Intro

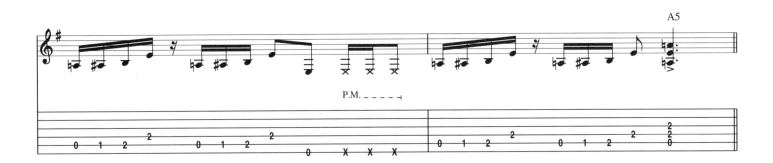

# Wall of Denial

**Written by Stevie Ray Vaughan and Doyle Bramhall**

Tune down 1/2 step:
(low to high) Eb–Ab–Db–Gb–Bb–Eb

Intro

# Wang Dang Doodle

**Written by Willie Dixon**

Drop D tuning:
(low to high) D–A–D–G–B–E

**Intro**

**Moderately** ♩ = 112

Em

Gtr. 1 (clean)

# We're Ready

**Words and Music by Tom Scholz**

**Intro**

**Moderate Rock** ♩ = 138

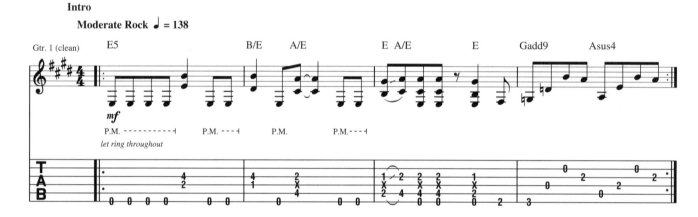

# What Would You Say

**Words and Music by David J. Matthews**

**Intro**

**Moderate Rock** ♩ = 120

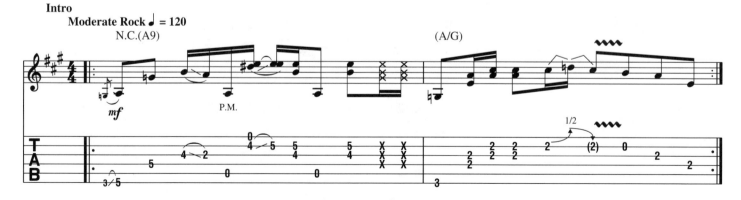

# Who Do You Love

**Words and Music by Ellas McDaniel**

Intro

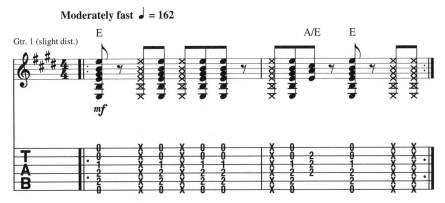

# Windy

**Words and Music by Ruthann Friedman**

Intro

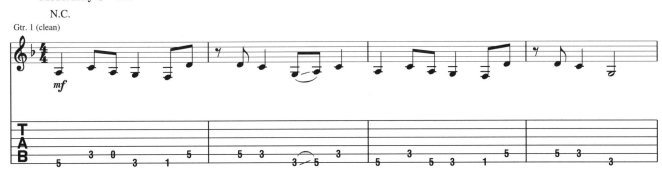

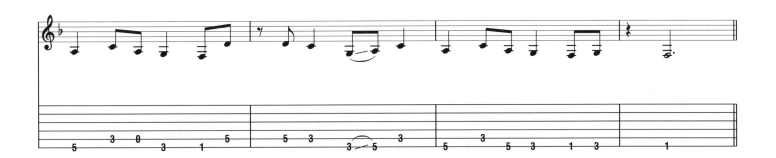

# Wonderful Tonight

**Words and Music by Eric Clapton**

Intro
Moderately Slow ♩ = 95
Half-Time Feel

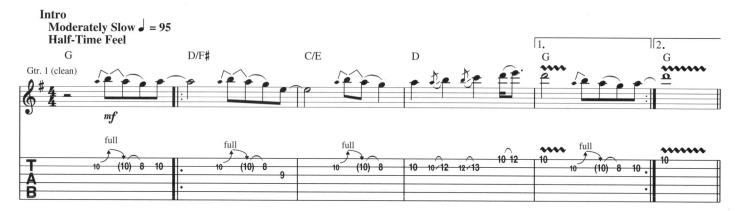

# Wonderwall

**Words and Music by Noel Gallagher**

Capo II
Intro
Moderately ♩ = 87

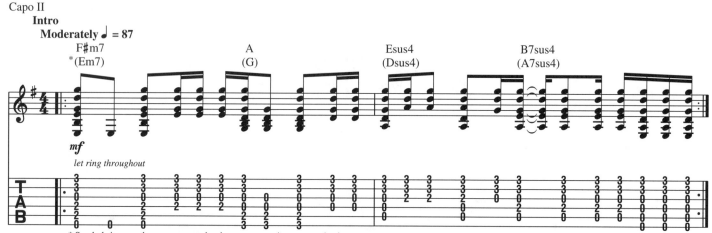

\* Symbols in parentheses represent chord names respective to capoed guitar.
Symbols above reflect actual sounding chords. Capoed fret is "0" in tab.

# Would?

**Written by Jerry Cantrell**

Tune down 1/2 step:
(low to high) E♭–A♭–D♭–G♭–B♭–E♭

Intro
Moderately ♩ = 100

# You Really Got Me

**Words and Music by Ray Davies**

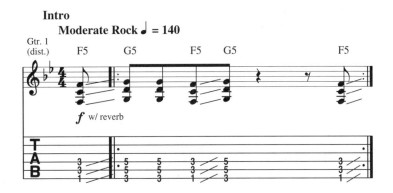

# You Shook Me

**Written by Willie Dixon and J.B. Lenoir**

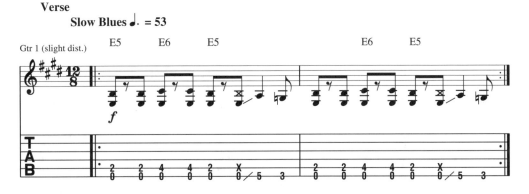

# You've Been Gone Too Long

**By Buddy Guy**

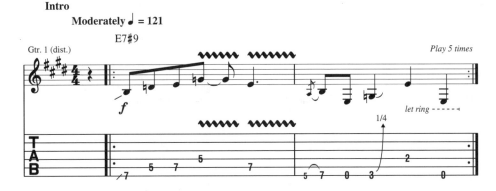

# Guitar Notation Legend

Guitar Music can be notated three different ways: on a *musical staff*, in *tablature*, and in *rhythm slashes*.

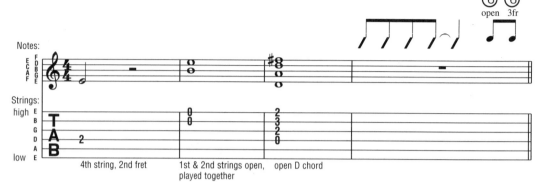

**RHYTHM SLASHES** are written above the staff. Strum chords in the rhythm indicated. Use the chord diagrams found at the top of the first page of the transcription for the appropriate chord voicings. Round noteheads indicate single notes.

**THE MUSICAL STAFF** shows pitches and rhythms and is divided by bar lines into measures. Pitches are named after the first seven letters of the alphabet.

**TABLATURE** graphically represents the guitar fingerboard. Each horizontal line represents a string, and each number represents a fret.

**HALF-STEP BEND:** Strike the note and bend up 1/2 step.

**BEND AND RELEASE:** Strike the note and bend up as indicated, then release back to the original note. Only the first note is struck.

**HAMMER-ON:** Strike the first (lower) note with one finger, then sound the higher note (on the same string) with another finger by fretting it without picking.

**TRILL:** Very rapidly alternate between the notes indicated by continuously hammering on and pulling off.

**PICK SCRAPE:** The edge of the pick is rubbed down (or up) the string, producing a scratchy sound.

**TREMOLO PICKING:** The note is picked as rapidly and continuously as possible.

**WHOLE-STEP BEND:** Strike the note and bend up one step.

**PRE-BEND:** Bend the note as indicated, then strike it.

**PULL-OFF:** Place both fingers on the notes to be sounded. Strike the first note and without picking, pull the finger off to sound the second (lower) note.

**TAPPING:** Hammer ("tap") the fret indicated with the pick-hand index or middle finger and pull off to the note fretted by the fret hand.

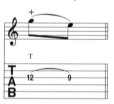

**MUFFLED STRINGS:** A percussive sound is produced by laying the fret hand across the string(s) without depressing, and striking them with the pick hand.

**VIBRATO BAR DIVE AND RETURN:** The pitch of the note or chord is dropped a specified number of steps (in rhythm) then returned to the original pitch.

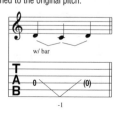

**GRACE NOTE BEND:** Strike the note and immediately bend up as indicated.

**VIBRATO:** The string is vibrated by rapidly bending and releasing the note with the fretting hand.

**LEGATO SLIDE:** Strike the first note and then slide the same fret-hand finger up or down to the second note. The second note is not struck.

**NATURAL HARMONIC:** Strike the note while the fret-hand lightly touches the string directly over the fret indicated.

**PALM MUTING:** The note is partially muted by the pick hand lightly touching the string(s) just before the bridge.

**VIBRATO BAR SCOOP:** Depress the bar just before striking the note, then quickly release the bar.

**SLIGHT (MICROTONE) BEND:** Strike the note and bend up 1/4 step.

**WIDE VIBRATO:** The pitch is varied to a greater degree by vibrating with the fretting hand.

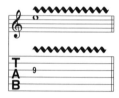

**SHIFT SLIDE:** Same as legato slide, except the second note is struck.

**PINCH HARMONIC:** The note is fretted normally and a harmonic is produced by adding the edge of the thumb or the tip of the index finger of the pick hand to the normal pick attack.

**RAKE:** Drag the pick across the strings indicated with a single motion.

**VIBRATO BAR DIP:** Strike the note and then immediately drop a specified number of steps, then release back to the original pitch.